The Essence of Maths Teaching for Mastery

- Maths teaching for mastery rejects the idea that a large proportion of people 'just can't do maths'.

- All pupils are encouraged by the belief that by working hard at maths they can succeed.

- Pupils are taught through whole-class interactive teaching, where the focus is on **all** pupils working together on the same lesson content at the same time, as happens in Shanghai and several other regions that teach maths successfully. This ensures that all can master concepts before moving to the next part of the curriculum sequence, allowing no pupil to be left behind.

- If a pupil fails to grasp a concept or procedure, this is identified quickly and early intervention ensures the pupil is ready to move forward with the whole class in the next lesson.

- Lesson design identifies the new mathematics that is to be taught, the key points, the difficult points and a carefully sequenced journey through the learning. In a typical lesson pupils sit facing the teacher and the teacher leads back and forth interaction, including questioning, short tasks, explanation, demonstration, and discussion.

- Procedural fluency and conceptual understanding are developed in tandem because each supports the development of the other.

- It is recognised that practice is a vital part of learning, but the practice used is **intelligent practice** that both reinforces pupils' procedural fluency and develops their conceptual understanding.

- Significant time is spent developing deep knowledge of the key ideas that are needed to underpin future learning. The structure and connections within the mathematics are emphasised, so that pupils develop deep learning that can be sustained.

- Key facts such as multiplication tables and addition facts within 10 are learnt to automaticity to avoid cognitive overload in the working memory and enable pupils to focus on new concepts.

June 2016

Is It True That Some People Just Can't Do Math?

How does the mind work—and especially how does it learn? Teachers' instructional decisions are based on a mix of theories learned in teacher education, trial and error, craft knowledge, and gut instinct. Such knowledge often serves us well, but is there anything sturdier to rely on?

Cognitive science is an interdisciplinary field of researchers from psychology, neuroscience, linguistics, philosophy, computer science, and anthropology who seek to understand the mind. In this regular American Educator *column, we consider findings from this field that are strong and clear enough to merit classroom application.*

BY DANIEL T. WILLINGHAM

Question: "I'm just no good at math." Every year, I hear this from at least a few of my students. In fact, I've heard it from plenty of adults too. Is there any truth to this notion that some people just can't learn mathematics?

Daniel T. Willingham is a professor of cognitive psychology at the University of Virginia. His most recent book, Why Don't Students Like School?, *is designed to help teachers apply research on the mind to the classroom setting. For his articles on education, go to* **www.danielwillingham.com**. *Readers can pose specific questions to "Ask the Cognitive Scientist,"* American Educator, *555 New Jersey Ave. N.W., Washington, DC 20001, or to* **amered@aft.org**. *Future columns will try to address readers' questions.*

Answer: While it is true that some people are better at math than others—just like some are better than others at writing or building cabinets or anything else—it is also true that the vast majority of people are fully capable of learning K–12 mathematics. Learning mathematics does not come as naturally as learning to speak, but our brains do have the necessary equipment. So, learning math is somewhat like learning to read: we can do it, but it takes time and effort, and requires mastering increasingly complex skills and content. Just about everyone will get to the point where they can read a serious newspaper, and just about everyone will get to the point where they can do high school–level algebra and geometry—even if not everyone wants to reach the point of comprehending James Joyce's *Ulysses* or solving partial differential equations.

* * *

"I'm just no good at math" is said so often—and with so little embarrassment (at least in the United States)—that it seems as though our society has accepted the "fact" that math is not for most of us. The problem is that this notion is a myth. Virtually everyone is fully capable of learning the numeracy content and skills required

2

A substantial proportion of both children and adults have cognitive and/or emotional difficulties with mathematics[4]; some studies find prevalence as high as 60% in university students (taking a range of subjects)[5], while others report around 25%[2,3,12]. Recent research suggests maths anxiety can begin much earlier than previously thought[12] (it has been observed in 5 year-olds) – and not just in response to complex mathematics, but also early number skills[9]. Girls report higher levels of maths anxiety than boys.[13]

IMPLICATIONS: A high proportion of students may experience maths anxiety – and not just older students working on complex maths

Girls are more likely to report maths anxiety

3

Maths anxiety is often self-reported, but more recently brain imaging studies have found a distinct pattern in those who report it, showing decreased activity in regions associated with working memory and numerical processing[8]. Maths anxiety appears to rob students of working memory, and affects those with high working memory the most[12]. Students who had maths anxiety but whose brains showed activity in areas associated with control of negative emotions performed nearly as well on a difficult math task as those without maths anxiety, showing helping students to eliminate the anxious response once it occurs can be effective.[8]

IMPLICATIONS: Maths anxiety affects the brain, particularly working memory; overtly helping students to deal with anxiety as it occurs can be effective

4

Maths anxiety can be transmitted from teacher to student[10]; teachers who are anxious or negative about mathematics can instil the same attitudes in their students[9]; there also seems to be a gender effect, where female teachers who are anxious about mathematics may have a negative impact on female (but not male) students' maths achievement and attitudes to maths[9]. Maths anxiety has been linked to intense feelings of shame or guilt, and can have a negative effect on teachers' performance as well as that of pupils; use of manipulatives in planning can decrease maths anxiety in teachers at the primary level[10].

IMPLICATIONS: Teachers who experience maths anxiety may induce it in pupils, especially female teachers and female pupils

Maths anxiety can inhibit effective teaching; use of manipulatives while planning may be useful

5

Students with early difficulties in numerical and spatial skills are more likely to develop maths anxiety – therefore interventions to help bolster these skills may help to prevent development of maths anxiety[9]. Students who believe they can improve with practice are much less prone to maths anxiety than those with more fixed beliefs[11]. Taking away time pressures reduces maths anxiety for pupils[12]. Using the Growth Zone model (considering one's own Comfort zone, Growth zone and Anxiety zone)[14] can help people characterise and deal with maths anxiety.

IMPLICATIONS: Early mathematics difficulty can be associated with maths anxiety; prevention of maths anxiety may be possible by bolstering early numerical and spatial skills

Promoting a growth mindset of mathematics learning, using the Growth Zone model, and minimising the number of time-pressured tasks for pupils may help to prevent maths anxiety

Lucy Rycroft-Smith, 2017

REFERENCES

1. Nuffield Foundation (2013) Understanding Maths Anxiety, [online] available at: www.nuffieldfoundation.org/understanding-mathematics-anxiety [Accessed 23 May 2017]

2. Ashcraft M.H., Krause J.A. (2007.)Working memory, math-performance, and math anxiety, *Psychonomic Bulletin and Review* 14: 243–248

3. Dowker, A., Sarkar,A., & Looi. C.Y. (2016) Mathematics Anxiety: What Have We Learned in 60 Years?, *Frontiers In Psychology* 7: 508

4. Carey, E., Hill, F., Devine, A., & Szücs, D. (2016) The Chicken or the Egg? The Direction of the Relationship Between Mathematics Anxiety and Mathematics Performance, *Frontiers in Psychology*, 6

5. Pérez-Tyteca, P., Castro, E., Segovia, I., Castro, E., Fernández, F.Y., Cano, F. (2009). El papel de la ansiedad matemática en el paso de la educación secundaria a la educación universitaria [The role of mathematical anxietyin the transition from high school education to higher education], PNA, 4(1): 23–35

6. Beilock, S.L., & Mahoney, E.A., (2015) Math Anxiety: A Factor in Math Achievement Not to Be Ignored, *Policy Insights from the Behavioral and Brain Sciences* ,Vol. 2(1) 4–12

7. Mahoney, E A., & Beilock, S.L., (2012) Math anxiety: who has it, why it develops, and how to guard against it, *Trends in Cognitive Sciences*, Vol. 16, No. 8 pages 404–406

8. Lyons, I.M. and Beilock, S.L. (2011) Mathematics anxiety: separating the math from the anxiety, *Cerebral Cortex*

9. Beilock, S.L., Gunderson, E.A., Ramirez, G., & Levine, S. C. (2010), Female teachers' math anxiety affects girls' math achievement, *Proceedings of the National Academy of Sciences of the United States of America*, 107(5), 1860–1863

10. Haciomeroglu, G., (2013) Mathematics Anxiety and Mathematical Beliefs: What is the Relationship in Elementary Pre-Service Teachers? *IUMPST: The Journal. Vol 5 (Teacher Attributes)*

11. Dweck, C. S. (2008). Mindsets and math/science achievement, New York, NY: Carnegie Corp. of New York–Institute for Advanced Study Commission on Mathematics and Science Education

12. Beilock, S., Willingham, D.T., (2014) Ask the Cognitive Scientist: Math Anxiety, Can Teachers Help Students Reduce It?, *American Educator*. 28–32

13. 'Devine, A., Fawcett, K., Szücs, D., & Dowker, A. (2012), Gender differences in mathematics anxiety and the relation to mathematics performance while controlling for test anxiety, *Behavioral and Brain Functions*, 8(33), 1–9

14. Johnston-Wilder, S., lee, C., Garton, E., Brindley, J. (2014). Developing teaching for mathematical resilience in further education, *7th International Conference of Education, Research and Innovation, ICERI2014, Seville (SFAIN)*, 2014

 CAMBRIDGE UNIVERSITY PRESS

 UNIVERSITY OF CAMBRIDGE Faculty of Mathematics

 UNIVERSITY OF CAMBRIDGE Faculty of Education

 Cambridge Assessment

ISSUE 6 MAY 2017

CAMBRIDGE √Mathematics ESPRESSO

RESEARCH, FILTERED BY CAMBRIDGE MATHEMATICS

TALKING POINT:

HOW DOES MATHS ANXIETY AFFECT MATHEMATICS LEARNING?

'For someone who has math anxiety, the anticipation of doing math prompts a similar brain reaction as when they experience pain — say, burning one's hand on a hot stove'
Sian Beilock

'interventions are easier and less painful if they take place before mathematics anxiety has set in'
Ann Dowker

THREE POSSIBLE THEORIES ON MATHS ANXIETY AND MATHS PERFORMANCE

① DEFICIT THEORY

② RECIPROCAL THEORY

③ DEBILITATING/ ANXIETY MODEL

Poor performance in maths

↓

Higher maths anxiety

Vicious cycle

Higher maths anxiety

↓

Poor performance in maths

Memories of poor maths performance generate maths anxiety

Higher anxiety contributes to poor performance; poor performance contributes to higher anxiety; a feedback loop is created

Maths anxiety reduces performance by causing avoidance of maths-related situations and cognitive interference

Adapted from ideas in Carey et al (2014)

IN SUMMARY

- Maths anxiety is associated with poor maths performance and the two could form a feedback loop
- Maths anxiety may be both mental and emotional; intervention should consider both aspects
- Maths anxiety appears to affect a significant proportion of school and university students at all ages, as well as adults; girls report it more than boys
- Maths anxiety affects working memory; addressing the anxiety and providing strategies to control it may be effective
- Teachers who experience maths anxiety may transmit it to pupils
- Use of manipulatives when planning may help to reduce maths anxiety for teachers

---

1 Maths anxiety is defined as a 'debilitating emotional reaction to maths' by the Nuffield Foundation[1]; other experts suggest it has both a cognitive and an affective dimension[4]. Maths anxiety correlates with measures of more general anxiety, but cannot be reduced to either general anxiety or text anxiety[5] and is not simply a proxy for low mathematics ability[8,12]. There is a negative correlation between maths anxiety and performance on maths tests[7], which has been explained by maths anxiety causing both avoidance of mathematical tasks and disruption of working memory[2,8,3]. Researchers do not currently agree as to which theoretical model might explain the link between maths anxiety and maths performance (see infographic) – whether the link is one-way, or a cycle.[4]

IMPLICATIONS: Pupils with maths anxiety may avoid maths tasks and experience cognitive disruption, which could form a feedback loop with poor maths performance

Maths anxiety may have both a cognitive and affective dimension; intervention should consider both aspects

---

CAMBRIDGE UNIVERSITY PRESS

UNIVERSITY OF CAMBRIDGE
Faculty of Mathematics

UNIVERSITY OF CAMBRIDGE
Faculty of Education

Cambridge Assessment

3

Early number learning seems to follow a very well-defined pattern, with clear stages. Infants can show surprise when the number of objects in a set changes unexpectedly, which demonstrates very early ability to count (eg Feigenson & Carey, 2003). Young children learn to recite numbers first without understanding their meaning, then they begin to fill this 'placeholder structure with elaborated concepts' – known as 'conceptual boot-strapping' (Carey, 2009). Young children can directly recognise (subitise) up to three objects, which usually increases to four with adulthood; they must understand the 'cardinal principle' – that the last word of a count is the total number of the set – before deeper conceptual number sense occurs (Sarnecka, 2015). Children from lower-income families tend to go through these developmental stages significantly later than children from higher-income families (ibid).

IMPLICATIONS: Research on number sense shows clear universal stages of development in early learning about number, which can help teachers to plan and assess.

4

If number sense is viewed as a skill set as opposed to something intrinsic, 'it should be teachable' (Gersten, Jordan & Flojo, 2005), although some researchers suggest good number sense 'cannot be compartmentalised into special textbook chapters or instructional units (Verschaffel & DeCorte, 1996) and its development does not result from a selected subset of specifically-designed activities – it may be better to see it as a 'by-product of other learning rather than a goal of direct instruction' (Greeno 1991). Good number sense appears strongly linked to high socio-economic status and therefore may also be linked to informal instruction at home; helping some students with specific aspects of number sense like quantity discrimination may help them quickly catch up with peers (Gersten, Jordan & Flojo, 2005). Effective use of board games with young children before they go to school can enhance early number sense (eg Siegler & Booth, 2004) and in the first years of school helping children make links between verbal and symbolic, digital and analogic representations of number can help develop number sense (Kalchman, Moss & Case, 2001).

IMPLICATIONS: Number sense is something that can be improved, although not necessarily by direct teaching. Moving between representations and playing games can help children's number sense development.

IN SUMMARY

- Number sense is defined by counting, comparing and flexible thinking about number, although some researchers don't agree on the exact definition
- Number sense is a foundation for maths learning
- Tests for aspects of number sense correlate strongly with later mathematical achievement
- Preschoolers generally learn about number in clearly defined stages
- Good number sense appears linked to high socio-economic status and these children also tend to go through developmental stages earlier
- Number sense can be improved by helping children make links and move between representations; board games can help

'People with number sense are those who can use numbers flexibly'
– **Jo Boaler, Stanford University**

'Rapidity doesn't have a precise relation to intelligence. What is important is to deeply understand things and their relations to each other'
– **Laurent-Moise Schwartz, mathematician**

REFERENCES

Berch, D.B.(2005) Making sense of number sense implications for children with mathematical disabilities, *Journal of Learning Disabilities*, 38:4, 333–339

Carey, S. (2009) *The origin of concepts*, Oxford· Oxford University Press

Case, L. P., Harris, K. R., & Graham, S. (1992), Improving the mathematical problem-solving skills of students with learning disabilities: Self-regulated strategy development, *The Journal of Special Education*, 26, 1–19

Feigenson, L., & Carey, S. (2003), Tracking individuals via objectfiles Tracking individuals via objectfiles: evidence from infants' manual search, *Developmental Science* 6:5, pp 568–584

Feikes, D. & Schwingendorf, K. (2008), The Importance of Compression in Children's Learning of Mathematics and Teacher's Learning to Teach Mathematics, *Mediterranean Journal for Research in Mathematics Education 7*

Geary, D. C., Hamson, C. O., & Hoard, M. K. (2000), Numerical and arithmetical cognition: A longitudinal study of process and concept deficits in children with learning disability, *Journal of Experimental Child Psychology*, 77, 236–263

Greeno, J. G. (1991), Number sense as situated knowing in a conceptual domain, *Journal for Research in Mathematics Education*. 22, pp170–218

Kalchman, M., Moss, J., & Case, R. (2001), Psychological models for the development of mathematical understanding: Rational numbers and functions, S. Carver & D. Klahr (Eds.), *Cognition and instruction* (pp. 1–38). Mahwah, NJ: Erlbaum

Leibovitch, T., Katzin, N., Harel, M., & Henik., A. *(in press)*, From 'sense of number' to 'sense of magnitude' – The role of continuous magnitudes in numerical cognition , *Behavioural and Brain Sciences*

Sarnecka, B.W. (2015) Learning to represent exact numbers, *Synthese*, pp1–18

Siegler, R. S., & Booth, J. L. (2004), Development of numerical estimation in young children, *Child Development*, 75, 428–444

Verschaffel, L., & De Corte, E. (1996)., Number and arithmetic, A. J. Bishop, K. Clements, C. Keitel, J. Kilpatrick, & C.Laborde (Eds). *International handbook of mathematics education* (pp. 99–137). Dordrecht, The Netherlands: Kluwer

Siegler, R. S., & Booth, J. L. (2004), Development of numerical estimation in young children, *Child Development*, 75, 428–444

 **CAMBRIDGE** UNIVERSITY PRESS

 **UNIVERSITY OF CAMBRIDGE** Faculty of Mathematics

UNIVERSITY OF CAMBRIDGE Faculty of Education

 **Cambridge** Assessment

ISSUE 4 FEBRUARY 2017

CAMBRIDGE √Mathematics ESPRESSO

RESEARCH, FILTERED BY CAMBRIDGE MATHEMATICS

TALKING POINT:

WHAT IS 'NUMBER SENSE' AND HOW DOES IT AFFECT MATHEMATICS LEARNING?

'We also know from research that a key focus for early mathematics is developing number sense, especially understanding number symbols, e.g. 'the fiveness' of 5'

(Advisory Committee for Mathematics Education)

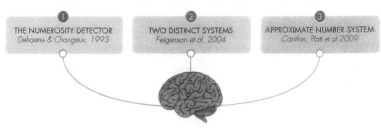

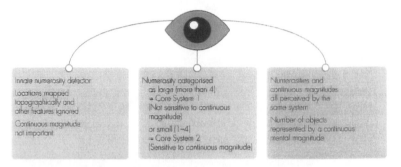

DIFFERENT THEORIES OF HOW WE PERCEIVE NUMBER

1

Number sense is a term that is defined differently by different experts – there is particular discrepancy between the two fields of cognitive science and mathematics education (Gersten, Jordan & Flojo, 2005). Kalchman, Moss & Case (2001) suggest there is some consensus on a definition that includes: fluency in estimation, ability to recognise reasonable results, flexibility when mentally computing, ability to move among representations and choose the most appropriate. Okamoto (2000, in Kalchman, Moss & Case, 2001) defines it as the two key skills of counting and quantity discrimination (comparing) – and crucially, the link between these two; these are the precursors to all the other elements. In this document, we use a combination of these two ideas to define number sense: in other words 'the ability to perceive, manipulate and understand numerosities' (Cantlon, Platt et al. 2009; Feigenson et al. 2004 in Leibovich, in press), which appears to be the most popular and well-documented definition.

The findings from experiments largely agree, with the disagreement often being about the models underpinning observed behaviour (see infographic; Sarnecka, 2015). While some researchers consider the origin of number sense a 'genetic endowment', others think it is an 'acquired skill set' (Berch, 2009), but almost all agree it can be improved through teaching in some way.

IMPLICATIONS: Number sense is not a term that all researchers define in exactly the same way, but includes basic counting and comparing skills and the flexible ability to compute and represent number. It can be improved through teaching.

2

Number sense is a foundation for all higher-level mathematics (Feikes & Schwingendorf, 2008) and a conceptual structure that relies on links between mathematical relationships, principles and procedures (Case, Harris & Graham, 1992). The maturity and efficiency of early counting strategies are predictors of students' ability to profit from mathematics teaching (Geary, Hamson & Hoard, 2000) and there are some key early concepts which correlate with later maths achievement: quantity discrimination, identifying the missing number in a sequence, and number identification, as well as working memory (Gersten, Jordan & Flojo, 2005).

IMPLICATIONS: Number sense is a foundation for higher-level mathematics and correlates with later achievement in maths.

CAMBRIDGE UNIVERSITY PRESS

UNIVERSITY OF CAMBRIDGE
Faculty of Mathematics

UNIVERSITY OF CAMBRIDGE
Faculty of Education

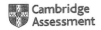
Cambridge Assessment

4

Some times tables seem to be easier to memorise than others (see infographic) and a structured progression of difficulty such as introducing 2, 5, 0, 1, and 9 first can reduce the amount of memorising for pupils (Van de Walle, 2004). Research suggests peer discussion, different representations and a broad selection of strategies are more effective than just repetition and practice alone (Brendefur et al, 2015).

IMPLICATIONS: Using a range of different methods and representations to help pupils learn times tables facts has been shown to be more effective than drill and practice alone.

5

Written tests sometimes fail to be good indicators of mathematical ability as poor performance can be due to slow processing, reading or recognising skills. When a significant amount of teacher time is taken up by excessive testing then formative assessment may be restricted in favour of summative assessment (Harlen & Crick, 2003). However, using multiple ways of assessing can give a more valid picture (Howell & Nolet, 2000).

IMPLICATIONS: Combining the results of formative and summative testing leads to a more reliable way of assessing recall of times tables.

6

Research shows that giving students progressively less time to answer multiplication questions forces them to move from inefficient methods to rapid recall; however more recent research suggests timed, online tests reveal some associated maths anxiety effects, whereas untimed pen-and-paper tests do not (Ashcraft, 2002).

IMPLICATIONS: Combining the results of formative and summative testing leads to a more reliable way of assessing recall of times tables.

'The DFE (should be) ensuring that assessment for pupils aged 5–14 is light touch and geared primarily to supporting and encouraging their progress.'
– Royal Society

'Educational research shows memorising supports understanding, and understanding supports learning'
– Charlie Stripp, NCETM

'It is not terrible to remember maths facts; what is terrible is sending kids away to memorise them and giving them tests on them which will set up this maths anxiety.'
– Prof Jo Boaler, Stanford University

IN SUMMARY

- Times tables should be taught explicitly, using a range of methods and representations

- Digital resources have been shown to be effective in helping pupils practise times tables

- It is advisable to balance the amount of summative testing pupils experience with formative assessment

- Pupils should be assessed in a variety of different ways

REFERENCES

Ashcraft, M. (2002) Math Anxiety: Personal, Educational, and Cognitive Consequences, *Current Directions In Psychological Science,* 181–185

Bratina, T. A., & Krudwig, K. M. (2003). Get it right and get it fast! Building automaticity to strengthen mathematical proficiency. *Focus on Learning Problems in Mathematics,* 25(3), 47–63

Brendefur,J., Strother,S., Thiede,K., & Appleton,S. (2015) Developing Multiplication Fact Fluency, *Advances in Social Sciences Research Journal,* 2(8) 142–154

Godfrey, C. (2001) Computers in schools: Changing pedagogies, *Australian Educational Computing* Vol 16(2), 14–17

Harlen, W. and Crick, R.(2003) Testing and Motivation for Learning, *Assessment in Education.* Vol. 10, No. 2

Hasselbring, T., Lott, A., & Zydney, J. (2005). *Technology-supported math instruction for students with disabilities: Two decades of research and development,* Washington, DC: American Institutes for Research

Howell, K. W., & Nolet, V. (2000) *Curriculum-based evaluation: Teaching and decision making* (3rd ed.). Belmont, CA: Wadsworth

Hunt, R. R., & Ellis, H. C. (1999) *Fundamentals of cognitive psychology* (6th ed). Boston: McGraw-Hill

Ramirez et al., (2013) Math Anxiety, Working Memory, and Math Achievement in Early Elementary School, *Journal of Cognition and Development,* Vol 14(2), pp187–202

Ruddock, G. and Sainsbury, M. (2008), *Comparison of the English Core Primary Curriculum to those of Other High Performing Countries* (DCSF Research Brief RBW048). London: DCSF

Van de Walle, J.A., (2004) *Elementary and middle school mathematics: teaching developmentally.* Boston: Pearson

Westwood, P. (2003) Drilling basic number facts: Should we or should we not? *Australian Journal of Learning Disabilities,* Vol 8(4), pp12–18

Wallace, Ann H.; Gurganus, Susan P.(2005) Teaching for Mastery of Multiplication, *Teaching Children Mathematics,* 12:1, 20–26

Wong, M. and Evans, D (2007) Improving Basic Multiplication Fact Recall for Primary School Students, *Mathematics Education Research Journal* 2007, Vol. 19, No. 1, 89–106

CAMBRIDGE UNIVERSITY PRESS

UNIVERSITY OF CAMBRIDGE
Faculty of Mathematics

UNIVERSITY OF CAMBRIDGE
Faculty of Education

CAMBRIDGE ASSESSMENT

ISSUE 1 NOVEMBER 2016

CAMBRIDGE √Mathematics ESPRESSO

RESEARCH, FILTERED BY CAMBRIDGE MATHEMATICS

TALKING POINT:

WHAT ARE THE ISSUES IN LEARNING AND ASSESSING TIMES TABLES?

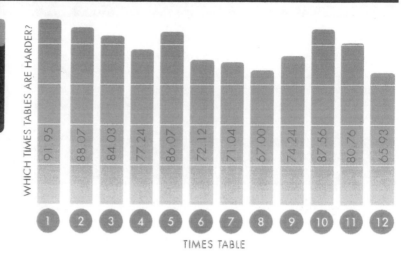

WHICH TIMES TABLES ARE HARDER?

Times Table	Accuracy
1	91.95
2	88.07
3	84.03
4	77.24
5	86.07
6	72.12
7	71.04
8	67.00
9	74.24
10	87.56
11	80.76
12	65.93

TIMES TABLE

PERCENTAGE ACCURACY ON TIMES TABLES TESTS (KS2 PUPILS)
(Guardian, 2013)

1

Facility with times tables facts is needed in order to perform higher-order mathematical processes efficiently (Westwood, 2003). Repeated systematic practice of times tables is effective and this declarative knowledge serves as a building block for procedural knowledge. This process is the key to making the retrieval of basic times tables facts fluent for pupils (Hasselbring, Lott, & Zydney, 2005). Times tables are the basis for further advancement in maths (Wong & Evans, 2007; Wallace & Gurganus, 2005) and nearly all maths curricula in high-performing countries contain the memorisation of times tables up to 10 x 10 (Ruddock & Sainsbury, 2008) but just learning times tables doesn't mean that a student will be good at later mathematics (Bratina & Krudwig, 2003).

IMPLICATIONS: Knowing times tables is important and should be taught in schools at a young age to ensure fluency for later mathematics, but it is not the only or most important thing to learn for early mathematicians.

2

Automatic memorisation of times tables frees up working memory to be used on other tasks (Hunt & Ellis, 1999). However, young children with a high proficiency with working memory (which also correlates with generally high academic performance, especially in problem-solving and reasoning) are prone to higher maths anxiety levels, which can have a negative impact on their achievement in maths by co-opting working-memory (Ramirez et al, 2013).

IMPLICATIONS: Maths anxiety can interfere with memory, which means testing times tables may create anxiety that skews test results and undermines confidence, a barrier in working towards automaticity.

3

Studies comparing computer-based practice of times tables with pencil and paper practice (e.g. Godfrey, 2001) suggest that computer-based practice is more effective, perhaps because students are more motivated.

IMPLICATIONS: Using ICT to learn times tables facts can be more effective and motivating than paper and pen methods.

 CAMBRIDGE UNIVERSITY PRESS

 UNIVERSITY OF CAMBRIDGE Faculty of Mathematics

 UNIVERSITY OF CAMBRIDGE Faculty of Education

 CAMBRIDGE ASSESSMENT

Rising Stars Maths

Problem Solving and Reasoning

Tim Handley

YEAR **3**

Rising Stars UK Ltd, part of Hodder Education, an Hachette UK Company, Carmelite House, 50 Victoria Embankment, London, EC4Y 0DZ

www.risingstars-uk.com

Reprinted, 2014, 2015 (three times), 2017

Author: Tim Handley

Consultant: Cherri Moseley

Publisher: Fiona Lazenby

Project Manager: Sarah Garbett

Editorial: Jan Fisher, Ethel Chitagu, Bruce Nicholson

Cover design: Words & Pictures Ltd

Design: Words & Pictures Ltd

Typesetting: Sg Creative Services

Illustrations: Tomek Giovanis

CD-ROM development: Alex Morris

British Library Cataloguing in Publication Data.
A CIP record for this book is available from the British Library.

ISBN: 978-1-78339-175-2

Printed by: Ashford Colour Press Ltd, Gosport, Hants

Acknowledgements

The authors and publishers would like to thank the staff and pupils at the following schools who trialled the *Problem Solving and Reasoning* resources and provided material for the Case Study conversation snippets across the series:

Bentley CEVC Primary School, Bentley, Ipswich
Bignold Primary School and Nursery, Norwich
Copdock Primary School, Copdock, Suffolk
Cutnall Green First School, Cutnall Green, Worcs
Delce Junior School, Rochester, Kent
Ditchingham Primary School, Ditchingham, Suffolk
Donington Cowley Endowed Primary School, Donington, Lincs
Eccleston C E Primary School, Chester, Cheshire
Garden Suburb Junior School, London
Gillingham ST Michael's Primary School, Gillingham, Beccles, Suffolk
Hapton CE VC Primary School, Hapton, Norwich
Harleston CEVA Primary School, Harleston, Norfolk
Piddle Valley CE VA First School, Piddletrenthide, Dorchester, Dorset
St Barnabas CE Primary, Warrington
St Francis de Sales Catholic Junior School, Walton, Liverpool
St Nicholas CE Primary, Hurst, Reading, Berkshire
St. Martha's Catholic Primary School, Kings Lynn, Norfolk
Well Lane Primary School, Birkenhead, Wirral
Woodlands Primary Academy, Great Yarmouth, Norfolk
Worfield Endowed Church of England Primary School, Worfield, Bridgnorth, Shropshire

Contents

Introduction

Rising Stars Maths *Problem Solving and Reasoning*

This resource is designed to help teachers develop a 'reasoning classroom' where problem solving and reasoning forms an integral part of each maths lesson. It provides key strategies to help teachers achieve this, together with extended investigation activities.

Problem solving and reasoning in the 2014 curriculum

The aims of the 2014 National Curriculum for Mathematics place a significant emphasis on the development of children's problem-solving and reasoning skills. Below are the aims of the curriculum, with the key elements relating to problem solving and reasoning underlined.

"The national curriculum for mathematics aims to ensure that all pupils:

- become **fluent** in the fundamentals of mathematics, including through varied and frequent practice with increasingly complex problems over time, so that pupils develop conceptual understanding and the ability to recall and apply knowledge rapidly and accurately.

- **reason mathematically** by following a line of enquiry, conjecturing relationships and generalisations, and developing an argument, justification or proof using mathematical language

- can **solve problem**s by applying their mathematics to a variety of routine and non-routine problems with increasing sophistication, including breaking down problems into a series of simpler steps and persevering in seeking solutions.

Mathematics is an interconnected subject in which pupils need to be able to move fluently between representations of mathematical ideas. The programmes of study are, by necessity, organised into apparently distinct domains, but pupils should make rich connections across mathematical ideas to develop fluency, mathematical reasoning and competence in solving increasingly sophisticated problems."

These aims extend problem solving and reasoning beyond simple worded problems, and it is expected that they will form a key part of the new statutory assessments at both KS1 and KS2.

Within the Programmes of Study, very few statements specifically related to problem solving and reasoning statements are provided. To help teachers develop a range of problem solving skills, suggested objectives have been developed and are provided on pages 14 and 15. For this reason, it is important that, when planning maths lessons, teachers always keep the aims of the curriculum in mind and incorporate problem-solving and reasoning opportunities into every lesson.

About the author

Tim Handley

Tim is the Mathematics and ICT Subject Leader at Woodlands Primary Academy, Great Yarmouth, Norfolk and is a Mathematics Specialist Teacher. He is also an accredited NCETM Professional Development Lead (Primary) – one of only a handful of classroom teachers with this status. He has a deep-seated passion for ensuring all children develop a true conceptual understanding of mathematics.

The publishers and authors would like to thank the children and staff at Woodlands Primary Academy for their support in developing these resources

How to use the resources

Structure

The resource is split into two sections:

1 *Key strategies*

2 *Activities and investigations*

At the back of the book you will also find a glossary of useful mathematical terms. All the supporting resources, including editable PowerPoint problem posters and Word files of the Resource Sheets can be found on the CD-ROM that accompanies this Teacher's Book.

Key strategies

This section provides 14 constructs or routines which can be used to integrate problem solving and reasoning into every maths lesson. Each Key Strategy is accompanied by a full explanation, tips for its use and a number of different examples of how the strategy could be used in different areas of mathematics to develop reasoning.

The examples provided are drawn from many areas of the mathematics curriculum. They are intended as starting points, which can then be taken and developed to use in all areas of mathematics.

Each strategy also contains a conversation snippet from a case study from the schools where these resources have been trialled.

Note that the content of some examples is pitched slightly below the equivalent year content objectives in the Programme of Study. This is to allow children to focus on the development of their **reasoning skills**, using subject knowledge with which they are already familiar.

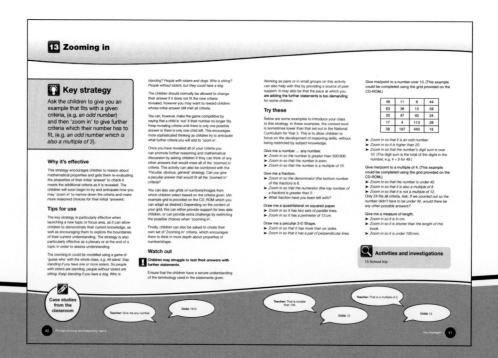

Activities and investigations

This section provides 18 extended problem-solving activities. These all develop one or more key problem-solving and reasoning skills, as well as, covering an area of the 2014 National Curriculum. Each activity will last a minimum of one hour and can in many cases, be developed further. The resources for each activity comprise:

- A poster to display on the interactive whiteboard to introduce the problem to the children. This includes the background to the problem, the main challenge or challenges, plus 'Things to think about' prompts to help develop children's reasoning skills. Where appropriate, definitions of any key mathematical terms are also included. Full colour versions of the posters can be found on the accompanying CD-ROM as editable PowerPoint files. They are also reproduced in The problem section of the teacher guidance for ease of reference. Some of the PowerPoint presentations include additional poster slides that can be used to aid differentiation by providing easier and harder versions of the problem.

- Detailed teacher guidance, which includes a learning objective, curriculum links, background knowledge and a step-by-step teaching sequence. The guidance also provides key questions to help develop reasoning (which use one of more of the Key Strategies). Ideas of how to adapt the activity for those that require further support and how the activity could be extended to meet the needs of more able mathematicians are also included.

- For some of the problems, additional Resource sheets that may be useful for the problem are provided on the CD-ROM.

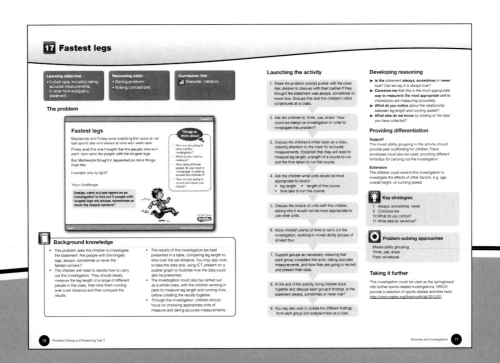

Maths superpowers CPD

John Mason[1] has identified a set of 8 'Mathematical Powers' that all children possess and which we need to foster and develop in order to create 'able mathematicians' who are able to reason about maths and problem solve. The powers, which come in pairs, are as follows:

Conjecture
Children should be encouraged to **make conjectures**, that is say what they think about what they notice or why something happens. For example, a conjecture made by a child could be, 'I think that when you multiply an odd number by an even number you are always going to end up with an even number'.

and

Convince
Children should then be encouraged to **convince**, that is to persuade people (a partner, group, class, you, an adult at home, etc.) that their conjectures are true. In the process of convincing, children may use some, or all, of their other 'maths powers'.

Organise
Children should be encouraged to **organise**, putting things (numbers, facts, patterns, shapes) into groups, in an order or a pattern, e.g. sorting numbers or shapes.

and

Classify
Children should then be encouraged to **classify** the objects they have organised, e.g. identifying the groups as odd and even numbers, irregular and regular shapes, etc.

Imagine
Children should be encouraged to imagine objects, patterns, numbers and resources to help them solve problems and reason about mathematics.

and

Express
Children should be encouraged to **express their thinking**, that is to show and explain their thinking and reasoning, e.g. about a problem, relationship or generalisations.

Specialise
Children should be encouraged to **specialise**, that is to look at specific examples or a small set of examples of something. For example, looking at the odd number 7 and the even number 8 to test their conjecture that an odd X even number = odd number. Children can also specialise in order to start to see patterns and relationships and make generalisations.

and

Generalise
Children should be encouraged to **generalise**, that is to make connections and use these to form rules and patterns. For example, from their specific example they could generalise that any odd number multiplied by any even number gives an even number. Children should also be encouraged to use algebra to express their generalisations.

These 'maths superpowers' have become the central foundation of many maths teacher development programmes, including the Mathematics Specialist Teacher (MaST) programme.

[1] Mason, J. and Johnston-Wilder,S (eds) (2004 a) Learners Powers in: *Fundamental Constructs in Education*, London:Routledge Falmer pp 115-142

Developing reasoning

Reasoning and conceptual understanding

Encouraging children to reason in maths helps to support children to develop a conceptual and relational understanding of maths: an understanding of **why** maths 'works', rather than just following a set of instructions. This leads to a far greater understanding and confidence in maths.

Developing a reasoning classroom

1   Initially begin by choosing a few of the *Key Strategies* provided in the first section of this resource and introducing them to your class. Many of these strategies, such as **Always, sometimes, never, Peculiar, obvious, general** and **What's the same? What's different?** can also be extended to form whole lessons in their own right, which may be useful when children first experience the strategy.

2   Allow the strategies to form part of your day-to-day questioning, so that children become familiar with using them. If these routines are used regularly, children will quickly get used to structuring their thoughts in this way.

3   Then begin to use the extended problems in the *Activities and Investigations* section. These provide opportunities for children to develop their reasoning skills over a prolonged activity. Each activity includes suggestions of how the *Key Strategies* could be incorporated to develop children's thinking as they work on the investigations.

Cross-curricular reasoning

Of course, children's natural ability to reason extends beyond mathematics. *The Key Strategies* and approaches explained in this resource can easily be used across the curriculum. For example, in a geography-based lesson the question ***What's the same and what's different** about these two settlements?* could be asked. Alternatively, in an English lesson children could be asked to identify the **Odd one out** of a selection of words.

Problem-solving techniques

The following offers a number of suggestions that are useful to consider when organising and supporting children to encourage reasoning in the classroom.

USE ME

When supporting children in problem solving and reasoning activities, the following stages, which form the 'USE ME' mnemonic are useful to follow.

- **Understanding:** Check that children understand the problem, activity or statement that has been given. Does it need re-wording or further explanation? Do they have the subject knowledge needed?

- **Specialising:** Start by asking children to specialise by looking at, or creating, one specific example. This then can be extended to looking at/creating a small group of examples. By specialising, children are more likely to be able to explore the structure of the mathematics, before widening out to make connections and generalisations.

- **Encouraging representations:** The use of representations is vital as they significantly enhance children's experience and understanding of mathematics. Representations can take many forms including Practical (apparatus such as bead strings, counters, cubes, etc), Recording/Jottings (such as number lines) and Internal (internalised versions of representations that children visualise and imagine). Children should also be encouraged to create their own representations. Encourage children to think about how they could represent the statement, or how they could represent specific examples of the statement.

- **Making generalisations:** After children have looked at, and often represented, specialised examples, they can begin to explore the connections between their examples. Can they make a statement that applies to all examples? If no generalised statement is possible, can they make a statement that applies to some examples (and define which examples this applies to)? Can they explain why it is not possible to make a generalisation?

- **Extending:** Provide a further, linked, question or investigation for children to explore.

Grouping for problem solving and reasoning

Teachers often ask how it is best to group children for problem solving and reasoning tasks. Variety is really the key here! Below are some forms of groups for you to consider:

- **Familiar maths partners** who children work with frequently in maths and with whom they are able to communicate well.

- **Pairs of friends** who enjoy working together.

- **Mixed-ability pairs or groups** which have often been shown to raise attainment for all children in the group: the lower-attaining children benefit from the peer coaching from the higher-attaining children, whilst the higher-attaining children have to extend their understanding and thinking further in order to explain it clearly to others.

- **Same-ability pairs or groups** also, of course, have their place, as they allow the task to be closely matched to the children's ability

It is important that children become used to working in different types of groups. In this way, they develop increasing flexibility and become adept at explaining their thinking and reasoning to a wide range of people. Different tasks will, of course, suit different ways of grouping.

Panic envelopes to facilitate self-differentiation

These are a great strategy to enable self-differentiation of problem-solving and reasoning activities. Inside an envelope, place one or more items that will support the children in carrying out the activity, then place the envelopes either in the middle of a group's table and/or on a maths working wall.

The content of the envelopes can be varied, and could include:

- Additional information

- Key questions to help develop thinking

- Conjectures for the children to prove/disprove

- Specific examples

- Partly or fully worked solutions to part of the problem

Give children the challenge of taking part in the activity independently, but let them know that at any point during the activity they can self-select to open the panic envelope and read one or more of the items that you have placed inside. Of course, adults in the classroom can also suggest to children that they may benefit from opening the 'panic envelope' if they become stuck while working through an activity. The content of the envelopes can be further differentiated for different groups of children.

Graffiti maths

Graffiti maths is an approach to problem solving and reasoning tasks which encourages children to think and work 'big'. It was developed almost simultaneously by a number of teachers, including Claire Lotriet and Geoff Barton in 2012 .

Graffiti maths involves children working together as a team on a problem or investigation, working on tables that are covered in 'magic whiteboard' sheets, large pieces of paper (taped down) or another covering which allows children to write 'on' the tables. Some teachers also choose to remove the chairs from the classroom, which encourages children to move around the table.

This approach encourages children to work together and gives them ample space to explore ideas, test out conjectures and make connections. The recording space is shared, which means that one child is less likely to take 'ownership' of it whilst others hang back and 'lurk' in the background. The act of sharing the recording space also encourages maths talk and creates a generally 'buzzy' atmosphere in your classroom.

Children can also move around and look at different tables and their recording, which can be a very useful plenary or mid-session activity.

Think, pair, share

This strategy is particularly effective during shared learning. This is a development of 'simple' paired talk. Ask a question (usually open-ended) and give children a period of thinking time (normally one to two minutes works best) for them to 'privately' think about the question or problem posed. Next, give children some time to discuss the question/thinking with a partner, before the partners share their thinking with another pair (so forming groups of four).

Envoy

This technique enables ideas to be shared between different groups. Having given children time to discuss their own thoughts, conjectures and generalisations in groups, each group then sends an 'envoy' to share their discussions with another group.

The envoy could be chosen by the group, or be selected by the teacher. By randomly selecting the envoy, you will help each group ensure that every child in the group understands the thinking, conjectures or generalisations of the group as any one of them may be called upon to explain them to another group.

As a further extension, the envoy can be asked to bring back a summary of the thoughts from the group they visited to their 'Home' group, so that the groups can consider new ideas and revisit their own thinking in light of the other conjectures.

[2] http://clairelotriet.com/blog/2012/12/15/graffiti-maths/

Snowballing

After giving time for paired discussion, the discussion can then be 'snowballed'. Ask pairs to share with another pair, and then these groups to snowball together and discuss with another group (forming groups of 8). Depending on class size, this can be repeated again (forming groups of 16) before each of the 'snowballed' groups feeds back to the whole class.

WWW and EBI as a plenary

A useful activity for the plenary session is to ask children **W**hat **W**ent **W**ell (WWW) about the activity and what would be **E**ven **B**etter **I**f (EBI). A ratio of 4 WWWs to 1 EBI is often effective, as this encourages children to focus on the positive and strengths from the session. The phrase of 'even better if …' encourages children to be constructive in their suggestions for improvement. So, rather than 'we didn't work together very well', children might phrase an EBI as 'It would have been **even better if** we had listened more to what each other said so that we could share our thinking together.'

Assessing progress

Accurate assessment of children's problem solving and reasoning skills is only possible through observation of and conversations with the child, together with evidence from their recorded work. The bank of evidence of a child's problem solving and reasoning ability will naturally be built up over time, as children experience and take part in a range of different activities.

The objectives in the chart on the following pages can be used when planning and assessing the problem-solving and reasoning elements of the new curriculum.

Problem solving and reasoning objectives

Year 1	Year 2	Year 3
• Describe a puzzle or problem using numbers, practical materials and diagrams; use these to solve the problem and set the solution in the original context.	• Identify and record the information or calculation needed to solve a puzzle or problem; carry out the steps or calculations and check the solution in the context of the problem.	• Represent the information in a puzzle or problem using numbers, images or diagrams; use these to find a solution and present it in context, where appropriate using £.p notation or units of measure.
• Order and arrange combinations of objects and shapes in patterns.	• Follow a line of enquiry; answer questions by choosing and using suitable equipment and selecting, organising and presenting information in lists, tables and simple diagrams.	• Follow a line of enquiry by deciding what information is important; make and use lists, tables and graphs to organise and interpret the information.
• Answer a question by selecting and using suitable equipment, and sorting information, shapes or objects; display results using tables and pictures.	• Describe patterns and relationships involving numbers or shapes, make predictions and test these with examples.	• Identify patterns and relationships involving numbers or shapes, and use these to solve problems.
• Describe simple patterns and relationships involving numbers or shapes; decide whether examples satisfy given conditions.	• Present solutions to puzzles and problems in an organised way; explain decisions, methods and results in pictorial, spoken or written form, using mathematical language and number sentences.	• Express the rules for sequences in words (e.g. 3, 5, 7: you add 2 each time).
• Describe ways of solving puzzles and problems, explaining choices and decisions orally or using pictures.		• Begin to make generalisations based on patterns in mathematics (e.g. all even numbers end in either a 0, 2, 4, 6 or 8).
		• Begin to make conjectures (statements) about mathematics and develop the ability to convince others (e.g. when continuing a pattern).
		• Begin to make 'if…then…' statements (e.g. if 2 + 4 = 6 then 6 − 2 = 4).
		• Describe and explain methods, choices and solutions to puzzles and problems, orally and in writing, using pictures and diagrams.

Year 4	Year 5	Year 6
• Represent a puzzle or problem using number sentences, statements or diagrams; use these to solve the problem; present and interpret the solution in the context of the problem.	• Represent a puzzle or problem by identifying and recording the information or calculations needed to solve it; find possible solutions and confirm them in the context of the problem.	• Tabulate systematically the information in a problem or puzzle; identify and record the steps or calculations needed to solve it, using symbols where appropriate; interpret solutions in the original context and check their accuracy.
• Suggest a line of enquiry and the strategy needed to follow it; collect, organise and interpret selected information to find answers.	• Plan and pursue an enquiry; present evidence by collecting, organising and interpreting information; suggest extensions to the enquiry.	• Suggest, plan and develop lines of enquiry; collect, organise and represent information, interpret results and review methods; identify and answer related questions.
• Identify and use patterns, relationships and properties of numbers or shapes; investigate a statement involving numbers and test it with examples.	• Explore patterns, properties and relationships and propose a general statement involving numbers or shapes; identify examples for which the statement is true or false.	• Represent and interpret sequences, patterns and relationships involving numbers and shapes; suggest and test hypotheses; construct and use simple expressions and formulae in words then symbols.
• Express the rules for increasingly complex sequences in words (e.g. 3, 6, 12, 24: you double each time).	• Explain reasoning using diagrams, graphs and text; refine ways of recording using images and symbols.	• Explain reasoning and conclusions, using words, symbols or diagrams as appropriate. Use simple formulae expressed in words. Express missing number problems algebraically (e.g. $6 + n = 28$).
• Report solutions to puzzles and problems, giving explanations and reasoning orally and in writing, using diagrams and symbols.	• Begin to express missing number problems algebraically. (e.g. $6 + n = 12$).	• Begin to use symbols and letters to represent variables (things that can change) and unknowns in mathematics situations which they already understand, such as missing numbers, missing lengths, arithmetical rules (e.g. $a + b = b + a$) and number puzzles (e.g. two numbers total 6, therefore $a + b = 6$).
• Continue to make generalisations based on patterns in mathematics.	• Continue to make increasingly advanced generalisations based on patterns in mathematics.	• Continue to make increasingly advanced generalisations based on patterns in mathematics.
	• Make conjectures (statements) about mathematics and further develop the ability to convince others.	• Make conjectures (statements) about mathematics and further develop the ability to convince others.
	• Continue to make 'if … then …' statements.	• Continue to make 'if … then … ' statements, representing them using letters if able (e.g. if $2 + 4 = 6$, then $6 – 2 = 4$ represented using letters: if $a + b = c$ then $c – a = b$).

1 Always, sometimes, never

 Key strategy

Give the children a statement and then ask whether it is always, sometimes or never true.

Why it's effective

This line of questioning encourages children to think about the concept of mathematical proof, and allows them to develop the key skill of proving or disproving a statement. It is also very effective in helping them connect different areas of mathematics and for encouraging generalisations and algebraic thinking.

Tips for use

This key strategy makes a particularly effective starter activity. It can also be effective when introducing a new focus or concept. It works particularly well if time is allowed for paired or grouped discussion, with the children encouraged to discuss the statement together and come up with their answer (always, sometimes, never) and justification before feeding back to you or the class. You can play 'devil's advocate', giving the children different examples to check against their decision. It can also work well to give children a statement about which they may have misconceptions, (e.g. *Does the answer to a question always follow the equals sign?*).

The strategy can also be used as a powerful assessment tool by asking the same 'always, sometimes, never' question at the start and end of the unit. Through doing this you should be able to notice and evidence the increased sophistication in the children's thinking and reasoning skills.

Children can also be given sets of statements to sort into 'always true', 'sometimes true' or 'never true'. These could be from one area of mathematics, (e.g. *fractions*) or a mixture of areas. Children can also be asked how the statements can be changed to make the always true, sometimes true or never true.

Children should also be encouraged to move towards generalised statements and, if they are able, algebraic representations of their answer, especially when the statement is 'always true'.

Watch out

Children may ask what you need in order to say that something is always true.

This can be used as a really effective discussion point about the nature of mathematical proof. Ask: *How many examples do you need to give to prove a statement is not true? What do you need to do to prove a statement is always true?*

Try these

Below are some examples to introduce your class to this strategy. In these examples, the content level is sometimes lower than that set out in the National Curriculum for Year 3. This is to allow children to focus on the development of reasoning skills, without being restricted by subject knowledge.

Is it always, sometimes or never true that when you multiply two even numbers together your result is even?
➤ *Let's multiply some even numbers together ... what do you notice?*
➤ *Why is this?*
➤ *What are you doing when you are multiplying? Could we write the multiplication as repeated addition?*
➤ *What do we know about what happens when you add an even number to an even number?*

 Case studies from the classroom

A snippet from a conversation between two Year 3 children discussing the question: *Is it always, sometimes or never true... that when you multiply two even numbers together, the answer is even?*

Is it always, sometimes or never true that taking away a 2-digit number from a 2-digit number gives a 2-digit answer?
➤ *Let's write down some subtraction number sentences.*
➤ *Can you think where this isn't true?*
➤ *What do you notice about the examples where the statement isn't true?*

Is it always, sometimes or never true that when you add a hundreds number (e.g. 300) to a 3-digit number only the value of the hundreds column changes?
➤ *Why does the tens and unit column not change?*
➤ *In a 3-digit number, what value is in the thousands column?* (0)
➤ *Can the value of the thousands column ever change when you add a hundreds number to a 3-digit number?*

Is it always, sometimes or never true that operations (e.g. addition) are commutative?
➤ *What does commutative mean?*
➤ *Which operations do we know are commutative?*
➤ *Why is multiplication commutative?* (link into being repeated addition, and therefore commutative as addition itself is commutative)
➤ *Is subtraction commutative? Why not?*
➤ *Can we think of another operation that is not commutative?*

Is it always, sometimes or never true that the answer always follows the equals sign?
➤ *What about if we wrote a statement like 7 = ? + 3 or 9 = 4 + ? ?*
➤ *What does the equals sign actually mean?* (a balance)

Is it always, sometimes or never true that the numerator of a fraction is smaller than the denominator?
➤ *Which part of the fraction is the numerator/ denominator?*

➤ *What does the numerator/denominator represent?*
➤ *If the numerator was bigger than the denominator, what would this mean?*

Is it always, sometimes or never true that you can multiply a number by 8 using doubling?
➤ *How else could you write doubling?* (×2)
➤ *What is 2 × 2?*
➤ *What is 4 × 2?*
➤ *How many times do you need to double to have the same effect as multiplying by 8?*

Is it always, sometimes or never true that a quadrilateral has four right angles?
➤ *Can we draw some quadrilaterals? Do your quadrilaterals have four right angles? How can you tell?*
➤ *What if you drew a quadrilateral whose sides were different lengths? Would our statement be true now?*
➤ *What special name do we give to quadrilaterals which do have four right angles?* (a rectangle)

Is it always, sometimes or never true that the perimeter of a quadrilateral is always an even number?
➤ *How do you find the perimeter of a shape?*
➤ *What do we know about adding an even number of numbers together?*

 Activities and investigations

Child A: I've done 5 × 5, and it's odd: it's 25!

Child B: But 5 is an odd number. I've done 4 × 4, 2 × 6 and they are both even.

Child A: Let's look at our multiplication square. I can't find any even × even that doesn't give an even answer!

2 Another, another, another

Key strategy

Give the children a statement and ask them to give you examples that meet the statement, and then ask for another example, and another … .

Why it's effective

This strategy encourages the children to give specific examples which meet a given general statement. By asking them to repeatedly give another example that meets the statement, they develop their skills of specialising, that is the skill of giving specific examples. This strategy also provides a good opportunity to assess their conceptual understanding of an area of mathematics.

Tips for use

Initially ask the children for one example that meets the criteria set, and then, after a pause, ask for another. Continue doing this, pausing slightly each time to allow the children to think about and construct their response, until they have exhausted the possible responses and/or a generalisation has been made.

You can focus the use of this strategy by introducing caveats. (E.g. *Give me another that involves a negative number.*)

This strategy can be used in conjunction with other key strategies in this book, including 'If this is the answer, what's the question?' and 'Peculiar, obvious, general (POG)'.

It is useful to analyse the children's methods for creating their responses – do they have a structured approach to generating further responses, are they using a generalisations, or do their answers appear to be given at random?

You should encourage the children to make generalisations by focusing on what their responses have in common. After generating responses independently, they could be encouraged to discuss their responses and draw out what they have in common. They could also discuss and compare their responses with a partner or wider group.

The activity can be extended further by asking children how many possible answers there are, asking them to convince you that their response is true. This is especially interesting if there is an infinite number of responses, as the reason for this can be explored. Mathematical thinking can also be developed further by asking children to convince you of the lowest and highest possible answers.

Watch out

 Children may stick to one rule/generalisation where there are other possible options.

Whilst the generating of generalisations can be a valuable outcome from using this strategy, sometimes this will not be the intended outcome and children will become 'fixed' on a certain rule or generalisation in order to generate each response. In these instances simply modifying the statement by introducing a caveat, as described above, is an effective way to focus children's thinking.

 **Case studies from the classroom**

A snippet from a conversation between two Year 3 children discussing the question: *Can you give me an example of ways to partition 192? Another, another, another … .*

Try these

Below are some examples to introduce your class to this strategy. In these examples, the content level is sometimes lower than that set out in the National Curriculum for Year 3. This is to allow children to focus on the development of reasoning skills, without being restricted by subject knowledge.

Can you give me an example of a multiple of 4? Another, another, another … .
➤ *What do your responses have in common?*
➤ *What if it your answer had to be a 3-digit number?*
➤ *What if your answer had to be a 4-digit number?*

Can you give me an example of an operation which is commutative? Another, another, another … .
➤ *Can you give me an example to prove that the operation is commutative?*
➤ *Why is multiplication commutative, but division isn't?*

Can you give me a way of partitioning the number 192? Another, another, another … .
➤ *What if it had to be partitioned non-canonically? (i.e. not down the hundreds tens and units boundaries)*
➤ *What if it had to be partitioned into four numbers?*
➤ *What if one of the numbers had to be 42?*
➤ *What if each number had to be less than 50?*
➤ *What if each number had to be above 60?*

Can you give me an example of a shape with a perimeter of 20 cm? Another, another, another … .
➤ *How do you measure to find the perimeter of a shape?*
➤ *What if it had to be a quadrilateral?*
➤ *What if it had to be a square?*
➤ *Are there any shapes that could not have a perimeter of 20 cm?*

Can you give me an example of fraction that is greater than $\frac{1}{2}$? Another, another, another … .
➤ *What if it had to be 8ths?*
➤ *What it had to be 10ths?*
➤ *What if it had to be 100ths?*
➤ *How can you make sure the fraction is greater than $\frac{1}{2}$?*

Can you give me an example of numbers that multiply together to make 24? Another, another, another … .
➤ *Can you give me a strange example that you think no one else in the class will have?*
➤ *What if one of your numbers had to be odd?*

Can you give me an example of a letter of the alphabet with one line of symmetry? Another, another, another … .
➤ *Do lines of symmetry have to be horizontal or vertical?*

Can you give me an example of a way of presenting data? Another, another, another … .
➤ *Do you always have to present data in a graph?*
➤ *Is there another way you could organise or categorise the data?*

 Activities and investigations

1   A brick in the wall ...
4   Alien farm
5   Number guess who
6   Missing problems
9   Remainder, remainder
10 Build a wall
13 School trip
14 Mystery shapes
15 Dotty squares
16 Cubed aliens
18 Chocolate swap!

Child A: You could do 100 + 90 + 2.

Child B: How about if we switched the 100 for two 50s, so it'd be 50 + 50 + 90 + 2.

Child A: Yes, that'd work, or we could change the 100 to 75 + 25, so it'd be 75 + 25 + 90 + 2.

Convince me

Key strategy

Make a statement to the children and ask them to decide whether it is accurate or not, then explain their reasoning to convince you.

Why it's effective

This key strategy encourages the children to look at the structure of mathematics and is another way for them to explore the concept of mathematical proof. Through trying to convince someone that a statement is true, the children will begin to make generalisations and develop their algebraic thinking.

Tips for use

This strategy is particularly effective when the statements given to children are statements which they 'take for granted' and assume are correct. Asking children to convince you that these are true, (e.g. *multiplication is commutative, i.e. 3 × 4 = 4 × 3*) will deepen their conceptual understanding of mathematics.

Whilst the strategy can be effectively used with given statements, perhaps the most powerful use of this strategy is in response to children's own statements and can sometimes lead to an impromptu, but valuable, diversion from the planned activity.

The strategy can be used alongside the 'Always, sometimes, never' strategy to help develop and prompt children's thinking.

When supporting children in responding to this strategy, the following 'USE ME' stages are often useful (see page 10 for more detail):

- **Understanding:** do children understand the statement?
- **Specialising:** looking at one or a small number of examples of the statement.
- **Encouraging representations:** *how could we represent the statement, or our specific examples of the statement?*
- **Making generalisations:** *by looking at our specialised examples, can we begin to make a statement that applies to all examples?*
- **Extending:** provide a further, linked, question for children to explore. This often works well when used in conjunction with other strategies from this book.

Watch out

! **Children responding with 'Because it is ... .'**

When children are first asked to convince someone that a statement is true, they often respond with a response along the lines of 'Because it is ... .' or 'Because my teachers have always told me.' Children can be encouraged to respond in the form 'It is true that ... because ... .'

! **Children not knowing where to start.**

First check if the children have the required prior knowledge and understanding to be able to convince you that the statement is true. If they do, then providing some initial probing questions, perhaps on 'panic cards' (see Problem-solving techniques on page 11), can help them to follow a line of reasoning.

Case studies from the classroom

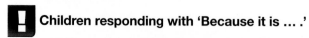 **A snippet from a conversation between three Year 3 children discussing the question:** *Convince me... that you can make an array to show any number.*

Try these

Below are some examples to introduce your class to this strategy. In these examples, the content level is sometimes lower than that set out in the National Curriculum for Year 3. This is to allow children to focus on the development of reasoning skills, without being restricted by subject knowledge.

Convince me … that multiplication is commutative.

➤ (<u>U</u>nderstanding) *What does commutative mean?*
➤ (<u>S</u>pecialising) *Let's look at an example. How about 3 × 4, which we know is the same as 4 × 3. But why is this the case?*
➤ (<u>E</u>ncouraging representations) *How could we represent a multiplication? Could we show 4 × 5 as an array? So, if we rotated our array (rotate by 90 degrees) that shows 4 × 5. What does the array now show?*
➤ (<u>M</u>aking generalisations) *Would this be the same for all multiplication facts? Can we always show a multiplication as an array?*
➤ (<u>E</u>xtending) *Are there any other operations that are commutative?*

Convince me … that some fractions are equivalent.

➤ (<u>U</u>nderstanding and <u>M</u>aking generalisations) *What does equivalent mean? What do we mean when we say fractions are equivalent?*
➤ (<u>S</u>pecialising) *Can you come up with any fractions that are equivalent to $\frac{1}{2}$?*
➤ *Can you use a diagram to help show that these fractions are equivalent?*
➤ (<u>M</u>aking generalisations) *How are these fractions linked? Can you create any other equivalent fractions? Do you have to use a diagram to help you each time?*
➤ (<u>E</u>xtending) *Can you write some fractions equivalent to $\frac{3}{4}$?*

Convince me … that squares are rectangles.

➤ (<u>U</u>nderstanding and <u>M</u>aking generalisations) *What is a rectangle? How can we define a rectangle? (A rectangle is any shape with four straight sides and four right angles.)*
➤ (<u>S</u>pecialising) *Draw me three different squares.*
➤ *So, does a square meet the definition of a rectangle?*
➤ (<u>M</u>aking generalisations) *So, could we say that squares are rectangles as they always have four straight sides and four right angles?*
➤ (<u>E</u>xtending) *Could we technically call a square a regular rectangle?*

Convince me … that multiples of 2 are also multiples of 4.

➤ *Can you give me some examples? Are they multiples of both numbers? Why would multiples of 10 also be multiples of 5?*

 Activities and investigations

Child A: I think it's only if you have even numbers, like 28.

Child B: Yes, you can't use them for 7.

Child C: But you could. It would just be a single line of 7 though. And 15 could be a 3 × 5 array.

4 Hard and easy

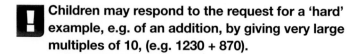 **Key strategy**

Ask the children to give you an example of a 'hard' and 'easy' answer to a question, explaining why one is 'hard' and the other 'easy'.

Why it's effective

This strategy encourages the children to think closely about the structure of mathematics and enables them to demonstrate a conceptual understanding of concepts. Children enjoy the challenge of coming up with 'hard' examples that still meet the requirements set out in the question.

The choices children make when responding to this strategy often provide valuable information about what they find difficult, which may not always be what you expect! For example, if a child constantly gives calculations involving decimals as 'hard' questions, then this would probably indicate they are insecure with decimal place value.

Tips for use

Unlike most of the strategies in this book, this strategy generally works best if children are encouraged to respond individually first. Once they have come up with their own 'hard' and 'easy' responses they should then be encouraged to discuss and compare these with a partner or larger group. The strategy 'What's the same? What's different?' can be used here to encourage children to compare and contrast their responses and draw out key themes/concepts.

Children should be encouraged to explain why the examples they have given are 'hard' or 'easy'. This could be by way of a written explanation or by convincing their partner/an adult verbally that their responses are 'hard' or 'easy'.

Watch out

Children may respond to the request for a 'hard' example, e.g. of an addition, by giving very large multiples of 10, (e.g. 1230 + 870).

Ask the children to convince you why this is a hard example, and then discuss how this could be made 'easy', e.g. by multiplying/dividing by a multiple of 10 and using known facts.

Try these

Below are some examples to introduce your class to this strategy. In these examples, the content level is sometimes lower than that set out in the National Curriculum for Year 3. This is to allow children to focus on the development of reasoning skills, without being restricted by subject knowledge.

Give me a hard and easy example of a 3-digit addition.
➤ *Easy: 100 + 300 as both numbers are multiples of 10 and 100*
➤ *Hard: 458 + 384 as the addition crosses the hundreds, tens and units boundary*

Give me a hard and easy example of a 3-digit subtraction number sentence.
➤ *Easy: 500 – 300 as it involves two multiples of 100 with a small difference*
➤ *Hard: 644 – 287 as it crosses the tens and units boundaries; 432 – ? = 121 as it is not in the 'usual' format for subtraction and involves a missing number*

 **Case studies from the classroom**

Give me a hard and easy example way to partition 389.

➤ *Easy: 300, 80 and 9 as it is partitioned along the hundreds, tens and units boundary (canonically)*

➤ *Hard: 100 + 124 + 35 + 130 as it is partitioned into four numbers, none of which are 'obvious' within 389*

Give me a hard and easy example of a fraction of number.

➤ *Easy: $\frac{1}{2}$ of 8 as it uses our known double/half factors*

➤ *Hard: $\frac{7}{8}$ of 63 as it has a non-unit numerator*

Give me a hard and easy example of a number in the 4 times table.

➤ *Easy: 4 as it's the first number in the 6 times table*

➤ *Hard: 76 as it's above 12 × 4*

Give me a hard and easy example of a sequence of numbers.

➤ *Easy: 2, 4, 6, 8, 10 as it has a single-step rule which is easy to spot (multiples of 2)*

➤ *Hard: 2, 6, 18, 54, 162 as it has a rule which is not immediately apparent (×3)*

Give me a hard and easy example of a shape to find the perimeter of.

➤ *Easy: as each side is the same length*

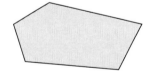

➤ *Hard: as it has sides of all different lengths*

Give me a hard and easy example of a question you could ask about this data.

➤ *Easy and hard answers will depend on the data/ chart you provide for the children.*

Give me a hard and easy example of a multiple of 3 over 100.

➤ *Easy: 300, as it is a multiple of 100*

➤ *Hard: 579, as it is not a multiple of 10 or 100*

Give me an easy and hard way to measure the width of this table.

➤ *Easy: using a ruler or a meter stick as these are standard units*

➤ *Hard: using cubes as we'd need a lot of them and it would be hard to keep them in lin*

 Activities and investigations

5 Number guess who
6 Missing problems
8 Fabulous 28
11 Fraction pictures
12 Money boxes
14 Mystery shapes
15 Dotty squares
16 Cubed aliens

Child A: 6 would be easy as it's 1 × 6.

Child B: Yes, or 60 as it's clearly 10 × 6.

Child A: Something over 60 would be hard, like 132.

5 # If this is the answer, what's the question?

 ## Key strategy

Give the children an answer. Ask them to come up with as many questions as possible that could have that answer.

Why it's effective

This strategy encourages the children to think creatively and explore the structure of the numbers and mathematics. The children will begin to spot and use patterns and through this make their own generalisations.

Tips for use

The children should be encouraged to share their possible questions in pairs and collate them together, explaining their possible questions to their partner if needed. Finally, each pair could be invited to share a possible question with the class, picking a question which they think no one else will have come up with. This provides a great opportunity for further questioning, which could incorporate some of the other key strategies, such as 'Convince me', 'Always, sometimes, never', and 'Another, another, another'.

Recording possible questions on a mind map, with the answer in the middle is an effective way to record responses to this key strategy. On-line collective canvases such as lino-it (www.linoit.com) and padlet (www.padlet.com) can also be effective to collaboratively record possible answers.

The children can also be encouraged to put their possible questions into categories. Some obvious categories could be questions related to division, questions which involve an odd number, questions which are in context, etc. However, asking them to categorise their possible questions themselves is often surprising and creates a good opportunity for further discussion.

The strategy can also be easily differentiated by adding set criteria to challenge or support children, e.g. only questions that involve addition, only questions that involve multiplication, etc.

The strategy also provides a great opportunity to encourage children to follow patterns. For example, if a suggested question is 4×2, can they also see that 2×8 and 1×8 are also possible questions?

Finally the strategy can also work well if it is run as a timed competition. Set a time limit and challenge children to come up with as many possible questions as they can, before then going through some of the follow-up stages suggested above.

Watch out

 Children may get stuck with one rule.

Sometimes children will get stuck with one 'rule' or type of question, e.g. addition questions. This can easily be overcome by asking the child to make their next question different: *What about a question involving a fraction? Give me a question involving a multiplication.*

Try these

Below are some examples to introduce your class to this strategy. In these examples, the content level is sometimes lower than that set out in the National Curriculum for Year 3. This is to allow children to focus on the development of reasoning skills, without being restricted by subject knowledge.

Case studies from the classroom

A snippet from a conversation between two Year 3 children discussing the question: *If the question is 26, what could the possible answer be?*

If the answer is 26, what could the possible questions be?

➤ Challenge: *Your question must include division.*

If the answer is 1, what could the possible questions be?

➤ Challenge: *Your question must include a fraction.*

If the answer is 'the ones digit is always odd', what could the possible questions be?

➤ Challenge: *One of your questions must be a generalisation about multiples of a number.*

If the answer is < 204, what could the possible questions be?

➤ Challenge: *Your question must include the = sign.*

If the answer is 600, what could the possible questions be?

➤ Challenge: *Your question must involve at least three other numbers.*

If the answer is 892, what could the possible questions be?

➤ Challenge: *Your question must involve the addition of two 3-digit numbers.*

If the answer is 7 cubes what could the possible questions be?

➤ Challenge: *Your question must involve division.*

If the answer is a 27p what could the possible questions be?

➤ Challenge: *Your question must involve the value £2.*

If the answer is a 3 hours 30 minutes what could the possible questions be?

➤ Challenge: *Your question must relate to the difference between two times.*

If the answer is a square what could the possible questions be?

➤ Challenge: *Your question must refer to angles.*

Child A: How about what is half of 52, as double 26 is 52?

Child B: Yes, and there are 52 weeks, so half a year... but that's not a question.

Child A: But we could ask, 'How many weeks are in half a year?'

Key strategy

Give the children a number, geometry concept or measure and ask them to write its 'story', that is as much as they know or can work out about it.

Why it's effective

This strategy encourages the children to explore everything they know about a mathematical concept and is therefore particularly effective at developing children's subject knowledge whilst also encouraging them to reason.

Through telling a 'story', the children are also likely to form and use their own generalisations and patterns, which can be a great starting point for further discussion.

Tips for use

Start by giving the children a number (which could include a fraction, multiple of 100 etc.), a geometry concept, (e.g. *a shape or co-ordinate*), or a measure (e.g. *an angle*). Then ask children to write as many statements as they can about the item given.

For example, when given a number the children may choose to look at the classification of the number (odd, even, square, etc.), the factors and multiples of the number, doubling and halving the number, sums and differences that lead to the number, statements that involve proportions of the number, etc.

As children create their 'story' they are likely to create and use their own generalisations and patterns. Discussing these with children using the 'What else do we know?' and 'What do we notice?' key strategies is particularly effective.

This strategy can also work well as an individual or paired activity, followed by a class 'race' to record as many different elements of the numbers 'story' as possible on an interactive whiteboard within a given time limit.

Watch out

! **Children may focus on one pattern.**

The children often get 'locked on' to one pattern, e.g. doubling and halving. Encourage children to explore other patterns by setting a target number of 'unrelated' facts that they record.

! **Children may 'run out' of facts to record.**

Sometimes children will appear to run out of facts to record. Draw their attention to patterns within what they have recorded so far and ask: *What else do we know?* A bank of prompt questions may also be useful, providing prompts for things to investigate, e.g. *What number is double the number? What are the factors of the number?*

Try these

Below are some examples to introduce your class to this strategy. In these examples, the content level is sometimes lower than that set out in the National Curriculum for Year 3. This is to allow children to focus on the development of reasoning skills, without being restricted by subject knowledge.

Case studies from the classroom

A snippet from a conversation between two Year 3 children discussing the question: *What is the story of 36?*

General prompt questions to use with number-based stories (including fractions).

➤ *What type of number is it?*
➤ *What is it a multiple of?*
➤ *What are some multiples of the number?*
➤ *What factors does it have? Does this mean it is a special type of number?*
➤ *Can you write this as a fraction/decimal/percentage?*

➤ *What is double the number? Double this number?*
➤ *What is half the number? Half this number?*
➤ *What happens when you multiply the number by 10? 100?*
➤ *What happens when you divide the number by 10? 100?*
➤ *What can you add together to make this number?*
➤ *What calculations could this number be involved in?*

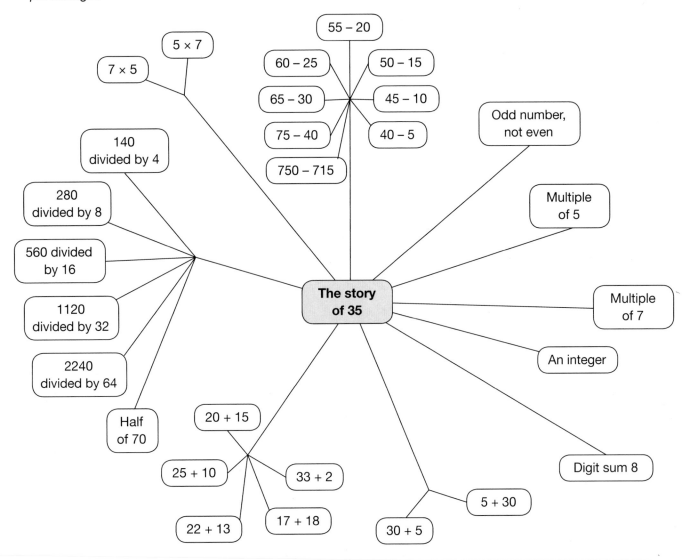

7 Odd one out

 ## Key strategy

Give the children a set of three or more numbers or statements and ask them to identify which number/statement is the odd one out and why.

Why it's effective

When the children work to identify what is the odd one out, they will be conjecturing and reasoning about the items in the set. Almost without realising it, they will create their own generalisations, and test all parts of the set given to them against this to try and identify the 'odd one out'.

Tips for use

This strategy works particularly well when time for paired or grouped discussion is given, with the children attempting to convince each other as to which item from the set is the odd one out.

To further increase the reasoning required, especially when the children have had some experience responding to this strategy, always aim to choose the set of numbers/statements you provide so that there is more than one possible 'answer.' This can create a good debate in the classroom, with different children trying to convince each other that the number they have selected is the 'real' odd one out.

This strategy could also be combined with the 'Another, another, another' strategy, by asking children to generate further examples that would either be similar to the 'odd one out' or to the rest of the set.

Watch out

Children may not see the link between parts of the set.

Sometimes children will struggle to find the odd one out as they cannot spot the generalities (links) between different parts of the set. Focusing children's thinking using the 'What's the same? What's different?' key strategy, initially with pairs from the set, can help children see the similarities and differences between parts of the set. Using 'panic envelopes' (see page 11) containing key questions to focus thinking can also be effective in supporting children to see the link between parts of the set.

Try these

Below are some examples to introduce your class to this strategy. In these examples, the content level is sometimes lower than that set out in the National Curriculum for Year 3. This is to allow the children to focus on the development of reasoning skills, without being restricted by subject knowledge.

Look at this set of numbers: 15, 16, 9, 3. Which is the odd one out?
Possible 'odd one outs' with reasons and key questions/follow-ups:
➤ 16: the only even number
➤ 16: the only number that is not a multiple of 3
Which times tables do these numbers appear in? Do any of the numbers have a common multiple?

 Case studies from the classroom

A snippet from a conversation between two Year 3 children discussing the question:
Look at this set of numbers: 15, 16, 9, 3. Which is the odd one out?

Look at this set of numbers: 9, 21, 36, 64, 81.
Which is the odd one out?
Possible 'odd one outs' with reasons and key
questions/follow-ups:

➤ 64: the only even number
➤ 64: the only number that is not a multiple of 3
  Which times tables do these numbers appear in?
  Do any of the numbers have a common multiple?
➤ 81: the only number greater than 80
➤ 64: the only number whose digit sum is not
  a multiple of 3 (This links into 64 not being a
  multiple of 3.)
  *What's the same and what's different about the
  total you get when you add the digits together in
  each number?*

Look at these shapes. Which is the odd one out?

Possible 'odd one outs' with reasons and key
questions/follow-ups:

➤ Irregular quadrilateral: only shape from those
  provided that does not have equal length sides
  What do we call shapes like this?
➤ Hexagon: only shape from those provided that is
  not a quadrilateral
➤ Square: only shape that has a set of
  perpendicular lines; only shape with right angles
➤ Irregular quadrilateral: only shape which does not
  have equal sized angles

Look at these fractions: $\frac{6}{8}$, $\frac{3}{4}$, $\frac{8}{10}$. Which is the odd
one out?
Possible 'odd one outs' with reasons and key
questions/follow-ups:

➤ $\frac{8}{10}$: only fraction that is not equivalent to $\frac{3}{4}$
  How do you know it is not equivalent to $\frac{3}{4}$?

 Activities and investigations

Child A: 15, as it's the only one that
is a multiple of 5.

Teacher: I wonder if there are any
other numbers that might be the odd
one out based on what they are a
multiple of ...

Child B: Well, because 16 is the only
even number, it must be the only
number that is a multiple of 2.

8 Peculiar, obvious, general

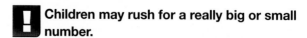

Key strategy

Ask the children to give a **peculiar**, **obvious**, and if they are able, **general**, example of a statement.

Why it's effective

This key strategy encourages the children to think about the structure of mathematics and the definition of the statements given. Through focusing on what makes a peculiar, obvious or general example of a given statement children have to think carefully about the statement given, the criteria needed to meet the statement, and what examples they could give. The encouragement to give a peculiar example encourages children to push the boundaries of their understanding, whilst the general example encourages them to begin to develop algebraic thinking.

Tips for use

This key strategy could be used either as part of shared learning, as the main activity in the lesson or as an effective plenary. The children should be encouraged to explain their choices, either verbally or in writing, which will encourage them to think about the definition of the given statement and the general structure of mathematics. The strategy works particularly well if they are encouraged to discuss and convince each other that their examples fit with the statement and are peculiar, obvious or general. When working in pairs, they can also be encouraged to think of reasons why their partner's responses may not be peculiar, obvious or general.

Encourage the children to first state record an **obvious** example. *What is the first example you think of? Why is this the first example that you think of?* They can always replace their obvious example with a 'more obvious' example whilst they are thinking through the activity.

Then ask the children to think of their **peculiar** example. Encourage them to think about the definition and criteria of the statement given. *What fits our definition, but isn't obvious?*

Finally, they should be encouraged to think about a **general** example. This will deepen their thinking about the statement given and their understanding.

Depending on the desired outcomes and ability of the children to reason, the requirement for a general example could be skipped.

Watch out

! **Children may rush for a really big or small number.**

In numerical questions, children will often state a really large or small number, which they arrive at by multiplying or dividing by 10, 100, 1000, etc. as their peculiar example. Discuss with the children if, just because an example is really large or small, it is peculiar. *What makes it peculiar? Is it really quite obvious as all we have done is multiplied/divided by a large number?* You can also modify the question to remove the temptation to go really large, e.g. *Can you give me a peculiar example of an odd number that is below 50?*

! **Children's general statements may not be general.**

Using the strategy 'Always, sometimes, never' to encourage the children to check their general statements can help children ensure their statements are truly general.

Case studies from the classroom

A snippet from a conversation between two Year 3 children discussing the question: *Give me a peculiar, obvious and general example of multiples of 4.*

Try these

The examples below were given by children who trialled this resource. Example follow up questions are provided where appropriate.

Give me a peculiar, obvious and general example of calculation that is commutative.
➤ Peculiar: 4 × 4 = 16 and 4 × 4 = 16 *How do you know this is commutative? Why is it a peculiar example?*
➤ Obvious: 2 × 3 = 6, 3 × 2 = 6 *Why is this an obvious example? Can you prove that these are commutative?*
➤ General: A number sentence where the order of the digits does not affect the value of the sentence. *Which operations are always commutative?*

Give me a peculiar, obvious and general example of a multiple of 50.

Give me a peculiar, obvious and general example of numbers with a product (the result of a multiplication) of 300.

Give me a peculiar, obvious and general example of a 3-digit addition sentence.
➤ Peculiar: *876 + 678 = 1554 as the numbers are the reverse of each other.*
➤ Obvious: *100 + 100 = 200 as it's a simple 3-digit addition sentence and the first one possible to make.*
➤ General: *Any addition question which involves the addition of two or more numbers with 3 digits.*

Give me a peculiar, obvious and general example of a fraction of a shape.

Give me a peculiar, obvious and general example of an equivalent fraction.

Give me a peculiar, obvious and general example of a set of three numbers with a sum of 20.

Give me a peculiar, obvious and general example of a quadrilateral.

Give me a peculiar, obvious and general example of shape with a perimeter of 8 units.

Give me a peculiar, obvious and general example of a pair of parallel lines.

Give me a peculiar, obvious and general example of a bar chart.

 Activities and investigations

2 Number aliens
8 Fabulous 28
11 Fraction pictures
15 Dotty squares
16 Cubed aliens
18 Chocolate swap!

Child A: Obvious would be 4 as it's the first multiple.

Child B: Peculiar would be a large multiple, like 224, as it'd take some work to prove it's a multiple of 4.

Child A: General would be any number which you could divide by 4 without getting a remainder.

9 Silly answers

 Key strategy

Ask the children to give you a 'silly' answer to a question and explain why it is a silly answer.

Why it's effective

By asking the children to give you a 'silly' answer to a question they will have to reason about the range which the possible 'correct' answers could fall into. This will require them to consider the properties that the question entails, and will involve them in making a generalisation about the 'correct' answer(s) in order to explain why their answer is silly.

Tips for use

Always ensure you ask the children to justify their silly answer and explain why it can't possibly be a 'correct' answer.

The children can also be asked to create a number of 'silly' answers and then to order them in order of 'silliness'. Encourage them to identify which 'silly' answer is close to the 'real' answer or involves a common error/misconception. This can be a great way to address misconceptions with children.

Modifiers can also be added to the base question to restrict the range of possible silly answers. Depending on the restrictions added, this can prompt deeper thinking and reasoning.

This strategy works well when the children are given the opportunity to discuss their 'silly' answer(s) and reasons why they are 'silly'. The strategy 'What's the same? What's different?' can be used to encourage children to compare, contrast and look for links between their 'silly' answers.

Watch out

Children may always give very large answers.

Children's natural instinct when asked for a 'silly' answer often is to go for a very large answer, (e.g. *4 trillion, infinity, etc.*). Depending on the question given, either ask children if they can prove that this is not an answer to the question (particularly interesting when the question relates to a statement, rather than a calculation) or place a restriction on the range of answers allowed.

Try these

Below are some examples to introduce your class to this strategy. In these examples, the content level is sometimes lower than that set out in the National Curriculum for Year 3. This is to allow children to focus on the development of reasoning skills, without being restricted by subject knowledge.

Give me a silly answer for a multiple of 4.
Prompt questions:
➤ *What is a multiple?*
Example silly answers and justification:
➤ **7**: as it is an odd number, and 4 only has even multiples
➤ **3**: as it is under 4, and multiples of a number are always over the number

 **Case studies from the classroom**

A snippet from a conversation between two Year 3 children discussing the question:
Give me some possible silly questions if the answer is 75.

Give me a silly answer for 323 − ? = 232

Prompt questions:

➤ *How would we work out the missing number?*

Example silly answers and justification:

➤ **100**: as that would be 223, as it's simple to take 100 away from a number

➤ **102**: as it's higher than 100. We know that 323 − 100 = 223, therefore the missing number must be less than 100.

➤ **87**: as the last digit is not 1. We know it must be, as the difference between the last digits in the two numbers we know is 1.

Give me a silly answer for **another way of expressing 6 × 4 = 24.**

Prompt questions:

➤ *How else could you express the number? Explore commutatively.*

Example silly answers and justification:

➤ **4 × 24 = 6**: as this clearly does not use the commutative law

Give me a silly answer for **a drawing of a quadrilateral.**

Example silly answers and justification:

➤ 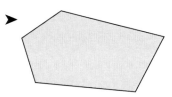 It is silly because it has more than four sides.

➤ 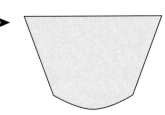 It is silly because quadrilaterals are polygons and therefore all their sides need to be straight

Give me a silly answer for an equivalent fraction to $\frac{3}{4}$.

Example silly answers and justification:

➤ $\frac{2}{4}$: as it has the same denominator as $\frac{3}{4}$ and we know that $\frac{2}{4}$ is equivalent to $\frac{1}{2}$ and $\frac{3}{4}$ is not equivalent to $\frac{1}{2}$

➤ $\frac{4}{14}$: as 14 is not a multiple of 4, and 4 is not a multiple of 3

Give me a silly answer for **the question if the answer is 86.**

Example silly answers and justification:

➤ **86 − 11**: as you are taking away a positive number from your target answer, which will always result in a smaller number

➤ **8 × 10**: as you are multiplying by 10, so you are making your starting number 10 times bigger, which would be 80, not 86.

 Activities and investigations

Child A: 75 + 9, that's silly because it starts with 75 and adds something to it so the answer must be over 75.

Child B: 65 − 23, that's silly as it starts with a number less than 75 and takes something away from it, so it's bound to be under 75.

Key strategy

Ask the children, 'What do you notice?' about a number, set of numbers, shape or mathematical statement.

Why it's effective

This strategy encourages the children to look deeper at the structure of mathematics. Through answering the question 'What do you notice?' children will be making their own generalisations and testing them against specific examples.

Tips for use

This strategy is very effective when children are given time to talk and discuss the statement with a partner or small groups, before feeding back to the class (larger group) with the expectation that they convince the larger group of what they notice.

When using this strategy, you can provide the children with sets of numbers/mathematical objects, (e.g. *3, 6, 9, 12; a rectangle, a square and triangle*) or general statements/properties, (e.g. *all multiples of 3, what happens when you multiply by 100?*).

Children's reasoning skills can be further developed by asking follow-up questions or providing follow-up statements once the children have responded to the initial 'What do you notice?' question. The strategy 'Always, sometimes, never' true often works well as a follow-up to a 'What do you notice?' question as this allows children to further develop their generalisations.

This strategy can also be used alongside many of the other key strategies, which can help to focus the children's thinking and reasoning.

Watch out

Children may not see the generalities.

Sometimes the children will be unable to independently state the generality or generalities relating to the statement which has been given. To help children see the generality, use follow-up questions, which could involve some of the other key strategies. 'What's the same? What's different?' is particularly effective here. Panic envelopes, with follow-up questions (see page 11) can also be used.

Try these

Below are some examples to introduce your class to this strategy. In these examples, the content level is sometimes lower than that set out in the National Curriculum for Year 3. This is to allow children to focus on the development of reasoning skills, without being restricted by subject knowledge.

What do you notice about multiples of even numbers?
➤ *Can you list some multiples of 2? Of 4? Of 8?*
➤ *What's the same? What's different about these multiples?* (all even numbers)
➤ *Why is this the case?*
➤ *What is another way of thinking about multiplication?* (repeated addition)
➤ *What happens when you add an even number to an even number?* (You always get an even number.)

 **Case studies from the classroom**

A snippet from a conversation between two Year 3 children discussing the question: *What do you notice about the angles inside a rectangle?*

What do you notice about multiples of 4?

➤ *Can you list some multiples of 4?*
➤ *What's the same? What's different about these multiples?*
➤ *How can you tell if a number is a multiple of 4?*
➤ *What numbers are all multiples of 4 also multiples of? How do you know?*

What do you notice about multiples of 3?

➤ *Can you list some multiples of 3?*
➤ *What's the same? What's different about these multiples?*
➤ *Find the digit sum of each of your multiples of 3. What do you notice? (Digit sum (adding the digits in the number together, e.g. digit sum of 27 is 2 + 7 = 9) is also a multiple of 3.)*
➤ *Can you use this knowledge to say if any number is a multiple of 3? Is 276 a multiple of 3? How about 1004? How do you know?*

What do you notice about this set of numbers: 50, 100, 150, 200 … ?

➤ *What would the next number be in this sequence?*
➤ *What would the 10th number in this sequence be? How about the 22nd?*

What do you notice about the angles inside a rectangle?

➤ *Let's draw some rectangles. What do you notice about the angles?*
➤ *Are all the angles the same size?*
➤ *What type of angles are they?*

What do you notice about fractions which are equivalent to $\frac{1}{2}$?

➤ *Let's list some equivalent fractions to $\frac{1}{2}$.*
➤ *What do you notice about the numerators and denominators in these fractions?*
➤ *Can you give me a peculiar, obvious and general equivalent fraction to $\frac{1}{2}$?*

What do you notice about what happens when you multiply by 10?

➤ *What appears to happen when you multiply 45 by 10?*
➤ *Does the same happen if you multiply 0.4 by 10?*

What do you notice about the perimeter of a rectangle?

➤ *Let's draw some rectangles. Let's measure the perimeters.*
➤ *What do you notice/what do you know about side lengths of rectangles?*
➤ *What are the lengths of each side of these rectangles?*
➤ *Is there any link between the lengths of the sides and the perimeter of the rectangle?*

Activities and investigations

2 Number aliens
4 Alien farm
5 Number guess who
8 Fabulous 28
9 Remainder, remainder
13 School trip

Child A: Look, they are all the same size.

Child B: Yes they are! And I think they are all right angles. They aren't smaller than right angles anyway.

11 What else do we know?

Key strategy

Give the children an 'If ... ' statement, (e.g. $\frac{1}{2}$ of 20 is 10), and ask them what else they know based on this statement.

Why it's effective

This strategy encourages children to see the links that exist in all areas of mathematics. It encourages them to reason and combine other known facts with the statement. This activity works particularly well as a starter or plenary, or as an early morning challenge.

Tips for use

Provide the statement and the allow children to record everything else they know. Adding a time and/or quantity challenge, (e.g. *Can you state at least ten other facts in two minutes?*) can help to add an element of competition!

Try asking the whole class to work on a statement individually, then to share their related facts with a partner, then ask each pair to share with the class a related fact that they think that no one else would have come up with. This approach pushes children to think deeper and go beyond the 'obvious' related facts. A mind map can be a useful tool for recording responses to this strategy, with children recording groups of related facts on each arm of their mind maps.

You can also work with children on the 'automatic' related facts that they should be able to state almost instantaneously, e.g. inverse facts, (e.g. $7 \times 8 = 8 \times 7$) and multiples of 10, (e.g. 70×8, 7×80, etc.).

The strategy can also be used with 'real-life' statements, e.g. *if we know that $\frac{1}{4}$ of a class are boys and there are 24 in the class, what else do we know?* (See exemplification below.)

The 'Peculiar, obvious, general' strategy can also be used alongside 'What else do we know?' to deepen the thinking from this strategy.

Watch out

! Children may 'stall'.

Sometimes the children will come up with a few 'obvious' related facts (perhaps using inverses, etc.), but then struggle to see any other related facts. Asking the children to discuss ideas together can help overcome this, as can encouraging them to 'combine' related facts, e.g. *use an inverse and also multiply by 10*.

! Facts/statements may not be related.

Sometimes the children will provide facts/statements that appear to have no clear relation to the given statement, but be careful not to say categorically that it is not a related fact. Instead, encourage children to explain how it is related, talking you, or another child through the steps they have taken to form this related fact. Analysing untrue 'facts' given by children can also help expose any misconceptions that they may hold.

Try these

Below are some examples to introduce your class to this strategy. In these examples, the content level is sometimes lower than that set out in the National Curriculum for Year 3. This is to allow children to focus on the development of reasoning skills, without being restricted by subject knowledge.

Case studies from the classroom

A snippet from a conversation between two Year 3 children discussing the question:
If we know that 450 + 350 = 800, what else do we know?

If we know that 5 × 8 = 40, what else do we know?

➤ 8 × 5 = 40, 80 × 5 = 400, 8 × 50 = 400 etc.

➤ 40 ÷ 5 =8, 40 ÷ 8 = 5 *Can we use our multiples of 10 and 100 to create other facts?*

➤ *How about using our doubling and halving skills?* 7 × 4 = 28, 7 × 16 = 112

➤ This could then be extended further, e.g. using inverse and place value with these double and halved statements, multiply by 4 and 8, etc.

If we know that $\frac{3}{4} = \frac{6}{8}$, what else do we know?

➤ *How are these fractions linked?*

➤ *Can you prove using a diagram that these are equivalent?*

➤ *How else could we generate other equivalent fractions?*

If we know that 340 + 320 = 660, what else do we know?

If we know that 1000 g = 1 kg what else do we know?

If we know that an odd number plus an odd number always equals an even number, what else do we know?

 Activities and investigations

1 A brick in the wall ...
4 Alien farm
7 Digit dilemma
8 Fabulous 28
10 Build a wall
12 Money boxes

Child A: We know that 45 + 35 = 80 as we can divide everything by 10.

Child B: Yes, as we also know that 350 + 450 = 800 as it doesn't matter which way round you do the addition, the answer is still the same.

12 What's the same? What's different?

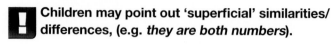

Key strategy

Give the children at least two statements, objects or numbers and ask them to compare them by asking, 'What's the same? What's different?'

Why it's effective

This strategy encourages the children to compare and contrast. It fosters children's ability to spot patterns and similarities, to make generalisations and to spot connections between different aspects of mathematics. The open-ended nature of the key strategy enables all children to contribute, regardless of their ability and support can easily be added.

Tips for use

Introduce the two (or more) things that you want the children to compare and simply ask 'What's the same? What's different?' This can work well individually, or through paired or grouped discussion. You could ask children to write their ideas on sticky notes, and share these together as a class, discussing each statement as it is shared.

The strategy can be used with two things, but can also be effective when used with more, as this can help develop children's ability to spot relationships. The strategy can also be used effectively alongside the 'Odd one out' strategy.

Key prompt questions can also be provided to groups who may need more support, or more generally when you need to scaffold the children's thinking in a particular direction. These could be provided on 'panic sheets' (see Problem-solving techniques on page 10) which children should use only if they cannot think of anything that is the same/different themselves.

Watch out

! **Children may point out 'superficial' similarities/ differences, (e.g.** *they are both numbers***).**

These should not be discouraged and the more often children are exposed to this strategy, the more 'mathematical' their responses will become. Providing prompt questions or panic sheets as described above can help children focus their thinking and produce deeper similarities/differences, which demonstrates a greater level of reasoning.

Try these

Below are some examples to introduce your class to this strategy. In these examples, the content level is sometimes lower than that set out in the National Curriculum for Year 3. This is to allow the children to focus on the development of reasoning skills, without being restricted by subject knowledge.

What's the same and what's different about 3 and 30?
➤ Same: both multiples of 3/ in the 3 times table, both have a digit sum (when you add up all the digits in the number) of 3
➤ Different: 30 is a 2-digit number, 3 is a 1-digit number

Case studies from the classroom

A snippet from a conversation between two Year 3 children discussing the question: *What's the same and what's different about 50 and 500?*

What's the same and what's different about 2500 and 4000?

➤ Same: both multiples of 100, both multiples of 50, both 4-digit numbers, both above 2000
➤ Different: 4000 is a multiple of 1000, 4000 is bigger than 2500
➤ Draw attention to how you can identify multiples of 50 and 100.

What's the same and what's different about $\frac{3}{4}$ and $\frac{3}{10}$?

➤ Same: both fractions, both a proportion, both numerators are multiples of 2
➤ Different: the numerators and denominators are not the same

What's the same and what's different about a cube and a cuboid?

➤ Same: both 3-D shapes, both have rectangle faces, both have six faces
➤ Different: cube made up of square faces

What's the same and what's different about a line graph and bar chart?

➤ Same: both show data, both are types of graphs
➤ Different: line graphs can be used to show continuous data, bar graphs cannot
➤ Explore the different types of data possible to display on different types of graphs.

 Activities and investigations

1 A brick in the wall ...
2 Number aliens
4 Number guess who?
6 Missing problems
7 Digit dilemma
8 Fabulous 28
9 Remainder, remainder
10 Build a wall
11 Fraction pictures
12 Money boxes
13 School trip

Child A: They are both in the 5 times table.

Child B: You mean they are both multiples of 5?

Child A: Yes, but they are worth different amounts.

13 Zooming in

💡 Key strategy

Ask the children to give you an example that fits with a given criteria, (e.g. *an odd number*) and then 'zoom in' to give further criteria which their number has to fit, (e.g. *an odd number which is also a multiple of 3*).

Why it's effective

This strategy encourages children to reason about mathematical properties and gets them re-evaluating the properties of their initial 'answer' to check it meets the additional criteria as it is revealed. The children will soon begin to try and anticipate how you may 'zoom in' to narrow down the criteria and make more reasoned choices for their initial 'answers'.

Tips for use

The key strategy is particularly effective when launching a new topic or focus area, as it can allow children to demonstrate their current knowledge, as well as encouraging them to explore the boundaries of their current understanding. The strategy is also particularly effective as a plenary or at the end of a topic in order to assess understanding.

The zooming in could be modelled using a game of 'guess who' with the whole class, e.g. *All stand. Stay standing if you have one or more sisters. So people with sisters are standing, people without sisters are sitting. Keep standing if you have a dog. Who is*

standing? People with sisters and dogs. Who is sitting? People without sisters, but they could have a dog.

The children should normally be allowed to change their answer if it does not fit the new criteria revealed, however you may want to reward children whose initial answer still met all criteria.

You can, however, make the game competitive by saying that a child is 'out' if their number no longer fits. Keep revealing criteria until there is only one possible answer or there is only one child left. This encourages more sophisticated thinking as children try to anticipate what further criteria you will add to 'zoom in'.

Once you have revealed all of your criteria you can promote further reasoning and mathematical discussion by asking children if they can think of any other answers that would meet all of the 'zoomed in' criteria. This activity can also be combined with the 'Peculiar, obvious, general' strategy. *Can you give a peculiar answer that would fit all the 'zoomed in' criteria?*

You can also use grids of numbers/images from which children select based on the criteria given. (An example grid is provided on the CD-ROM which you can adapt as desired.) Depending on the content of your grid, this can either provide support for less able children, or can provide extra challenge by restricting the possible choices when 'zooming in'.

Finally, children can also be asked to create their own set of 'Zooming in' criteria, which encourages them to think in more depth about properties of number/shape.

Watch out

Children may struggle to test their answers with further statements.

Ensure that the children have a secure understanding of the terminology used in the statements given.

Case studies from the classroom

Teacher: Give me any number.

Child: 7812

Working as pairs or in small groups on this activity can also help with this by providing a source of peer support. It may also be that the pace at which you are adding the further statements is too demanding for some children.

Try these

Below are some examples to introduce your class to this strategy. In these examples, the content level is sometimes lower than that set out in the National Curriculum for Year 3. This is to allow children to focus on the development of reasoning skills, without being restricted by subject knowledge.

Give me a number … any number.
➤ *Zoom in so the number is greater than 500/800.*
➤ *Zoom in so that the number is even.*
➤ *Zoom in so that the number is a multiple of 10.*

Give me a fraction.
➤ *Zoom in so the denominator (the bottom number of the fraction) is 6.*
➤ *Zoom in so that the numerator (the top number of a fraction) is greater than 2.*
➤ *What fraction have you been left with?*

Draw me a quadrilateral on squared paper.
➤ *Zoom in so it has two sets of parallel lines.*
➤ *Zoom in so it has a perimeter of 12 cm.*

Draw me a peculiar 2-D Shape.
➤ *Zoom in so that it has more than six sides.*
➤ *Zoom in so that it has a pair of perpendicular lines.*

Give me/point to a number over 10. (This example could be completed using the grid provided on the CD-ROM.)

48	11	8	44
63	36	12	58
20	47	40	24
17	4	113	28
56	187	440	16

➤ *Zoom in so that it is an odd number.*
➤ *Zoom in so it is higher than 20.*
➤ *Zoom in so that the number's digit sum is over 10. (The digit sum is the total of the digits in the number, e.g. 4 + 9 for 49.)*

Give me/point to a multiple of 4. (This example could be completed using the grid provided on the CD-ROM.)
➤ *Zoom in so that the number is under 40.*
➤ *Zoom in so that it is also a multiple of 8*
➤ *Zoom in so that it is not a multiple of 12.*
Only 24 fits all criteria. Ask: *If we zoomed out so the number didn't have to be under 40, would there be any other possible answers?*

Give me a measure of length.
➤ *Zoom in so it is in cm.*
➤ *Zoom in so it is shorter than the length of this book.*
➤ *Zoom in so it is under 100 mm.*

 Activities and investigations

13 School trip

Teacher: That is smaller than 100.

Child: 12

Teacher: That is a multiple of 2.

Child: 12

14 Other key questions

 Key strategy

In addition to the key strategies outlined, the following question structures can also help embed problem solving and reasoning into day-to-day maths teaching.

Can you give me an example of ... ?
➤ *a multiple of 50*
➤ *an irregular polygon*
➤ *two fractions that are equivalent*

What is the quickest or easiest way to ... ?
➤ *multiply TU × U (e.g. 34 × 6)*
➤ *multiply a number by 8*
➤ *find out a fraction of a number*

What is/are ... an example of?
➤ *150, 300, 450* (multiples of 50)
➤ *oblong, square, rhombus* (types of quadrilateral)
➤ $\frac{3}{4}$ (a fraction)

How can we be sure that ... ?
➤ *all multiples of 4 are multiples of 2*
➤ *multiples of 100 are also multiples of 50*
➤ $\frac{3}{4}$ *is equal to* $\frac{6}{8}$

Is ... a good explanation of ... ?
➤ *part of a whole ... a fraction*
➤ *number where the ones digit is an even number ... multiples of 4*
➤ *adding a 0 on the end of the number ... when multiplying by 10* (No, consider what happens when you multiply 0.5 x 10.)

What's the link between ... ?
➤ *3, 5, 7, and 11*
➤ $\frac{3}{4}, \frac{6}{8}, \frac{9}{18}$
➤ *an oblong and square*

Activities and investigations

Problem 1

A brick in the wall ...

Look at this brick pyramid. Can you see how it is made?

Learning objective
• Investigate number patterns.

Reasoning skills
• Making connections
• Working systematically
• Conjecturing and convincing

Curriculum link
 Addition and subtraction: solve multi-step problems

The problem

A brick in the wall ...

Look at this brick pyramid. Can you see how it is made?

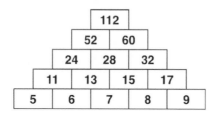

Each brick is the total of the two bricks that are below it. So the brick with the value of 11 is the total of 5 + 6.

This leads to some interesting patterns!

Things to think about

• How does the pyramid work? What does this tell you about the arrangements of numbers needed to give the biggest total at the top?
• How does the order of the bottom numbers effect the top number?
• Does your solution to this problem apply for other sets of starting numbers?

Your challenge

Investigate what happens when you create a brick pyramid using the numbers 1, 2, 3, 4, 5 in the bottom bricks (in any order). Which arrangements of the numbers will lead to the biggest total in the top brick?

RISING★STARS
Maths

Year 3   Problem Solving and Reasoning

Background knowledge

• Children to investigate number patterns formed by arranging 'bricks' into a pyramid.
• The pyramid has five bricks at its base. The number of bricks on each row above the base then decrease by one.
• The value of the bricks on rows 2–5 are formed by adding the values of the two bricks below the brick, ultimately resulting in a single brick at the top of the pyramid.
• Children are asked to investigate this number pattern using the numbers 1, 2, 3, 4 and 5 as their base numbers. These numbers can be placed in any order.
• Children are specifically asked to work out which arrangements of the numbers 1– 5 on the bottom of the pyramid will result in the

greatest total on the top brick.
• The arrangement which does this is 1, 3, 5, 4, 2 (or 1, 4, 5, 3, 2; 2, 4, 5, 3, 1; 2, 3, 5, 4, 1) all of which give the total of 61 in the top brick. (See problem 1b for answers).
• This arrangement with the highest number (5) in the middle, the next two highest (3 and 4) on each side, and the two lowest (1 and 2) on each end, will always give the highest possible total. Although this would be beyond most Year 3 children, you can see this would be the case by representing the wall algebraically. (see Resource sheet 1.2, Brick wall pyramid answers).
• Resource sheet 1.1 provides blank brick wall pyramids to assist children with recording.

Launching the activity

1. Introduce the problem by sharing poster 1b with the children, which just shows the pyramid with no explanation. In pairs ask the children what they notice about the pyramid.

2. Discuss what the children notice about the pyramid. Draw attention to how the numbers in the bricks of the pyramid have been calculated.

3. Share the prompt poster with the children. Ask them to discuss with a partner how they think they could make the biggest number in the top brick.

4. Discuss this as a class, recording any conjectures.

5. Provide time for the children to work on the problem with a partner or in small groups. As well as exploring which arrangements create the highest total, remind children to also keep note of anything else they noticed about the pyramid patterns.

6. At the end of the session bring the children back together and discuss which arrangements of the numbers 1–5 give the highest total in the top brick. Explore how there are multiple arrangements that give the same total, but ask, 'what's the same, what's different' about the arrangements. Also ask children to share what else they have noticed about this number pattern.

Developing reasoning

➤ *What's the same? What's different* between these two arrangements of numbers?
➤ *Convince me* that this gives the highest possible total.
➤ Which of these arrangements is the *odd one out* and why?
➤ Give me a *silly answer* for the arrangement that gives the highest possible total. What makes it silly?

➤ Give an arrangement of the numbers 1–5 in the bottom bricks. *Another, another, another.*
➤ If we know the best arrangements for the digits 1-5, *what else do we know?*

Providing differentiation

Support
Children could work on a smaller version of the pyramid (Resource sheet 1.3 contains a version of a blank pyramid with three rows). Children should initially use the digits 1, 2, 3, extending to the larger pyramid if able. It is also important to ensure that children have access to a range of familiar representations to help with the addition involved in this activity.

Extension
Children should be encouraged to generalise their findings from this problem and be able to arrange any set of numbers into the order that would give the highest total at the top of the pyramid. If the children are secure with this generalisation, they may wish to consider how this would extend to a 6, 5, 4, 3, 2, 1 or 7, 6, 5, 4, 3, 2, 1 pyramid.

Key strategies

2 Another, another, another
3 Convince me
7 Odd one out
9 Silly answers
11 What else do we know?
12 What's the same? What's different?

Problem-solving approaches

Small group work
Think, pair, share

Taking it further

This activity could be used as a springboard to further work on properties of number and number patterns. The children could also explore a multiplication pyramid with the brick being the product of the numbers below, starting with the three base pyramid.

2 Number aliens

Learning objective
- Solve problems involving addition.

Reasoning skills
- Solving problems
- Working systematically
- Conjecturing and convincing

Curriculum link
 Addition and subtraction: fractions and decimals (extension)

The problem

Problem 2a

Number aliens (1)

For this challenge your teacher will give you a series of connecting cubes. Each cube has the value shown below.

You need to build an alien out of the cubes with the cubes you use in the alien totalling 882.

- Red = 85
- Blue = 68
- Yellow = 17
- Green = 62
- Brown = 9
- Black = 11
- Any other colour = 0

Things to think about

- How are you going to make sure your alien has the correct total?
- How many different ways are there to make an alien that totals 882, if the cubes have the values that are shown on this poster?
- Can you create a new alien by exchanging cubes?

Your challenge

Create as many different aliens as you can out of cubes which total 882.

 RISING STARS
Maths

Year 3

Problem Solving and Reasoning

Background knowledge

- You will need to provide children with a selection of coloured interlocking cubes (or any other coloured construction toy).
- This activity asks the children to create an alien out of the cubes. Each cube is assigned a value and the children have a target which their alien must be worth.
- There are three different sets of this prompt:
  1. Problem 2a, which requires the addition of multiple TO numbers to make a total under 1000.
  2. Problem 2b requires the addition of multiple TO numbers to make a total over 1000.
  3. Problem 2c introduces the basic addition of decimals (.5) and TO numbers to make a total under 1000.

- The target values contained on the posters are achievable by using more than one combination of the cubes.
- The values on all the problem posters are 'exchangeable', whilst keeping the overall value of the 'alien' the same. For example, a red cube, worth 85, can be exchanged with a blue (68) and yellow (17) cube.
- Each version of the posters include a 'free' colour which does not have a value. This is to help put the 'finishing touches' to an alien and move the main focus onto the maths, rather than the alien shape!
- This activity works well independently or in pairs. Working in pairs provides opportunities for discussion around the 'Things to think about' prompts on the posters, whilst working independently allows for a more accurate assessment of children's addition skills.

Launching the activity

1. Begin by introducing the problem using the prompt poster.

2. Ask children to discuss the problem with a partner. *What would the best way be to attempt the problem?*

3. Discuss ways of tackling the problem together as a class. Ask, *Do you think there would be more than one way to make an alien with this value?*

4. Allow the children time to work independently, or in pairs, on their aliens.

5. If children complete one alien, ask them to consider how they could easily create a different alien which still has the same overall value.

6. At the end of the activity, ask children to compare alien designs and discuss 'What's the same? What's different?' between the cubes used in each design.

Developing reasoning

➤ *What do you notice about the value of the cubes?*
➤ *What's the same? What's different between your alien and your partners?*
➤ *Give me a peculiar, obvious (and general) alien that meets the target value.*
➤ *Give me a silly answer for a set of cubes to use. Why is this silly?*
➤ *Convince me that your alien will/does add up to the target value.*

Providing differentiation

Support
The values provided on the posters can be edited so that this activity is accessible for all children in your class. Ensure children have access to a wide range of representations to help them calculate the totals.

Extension
Add additional constraints to the activity, for example, on poster 2c, it could be said that only one green cube can be used, or that a minimum of three red cubes must be used.

 ## Key strategies

3 Convince me
8 Peculiar, obvious, general
9 Silly answers
10 What do you notice?
12 What's the same? What's different?

 ## Problem-solving approaches

Paired work
Snowballing
Envoys

Taking it further

The base activity could be adapted for other areas of maths, e.g. the cubes could be given fraction values in order to explore the addition of fractions.

<table>
<tr><td>

Learning objective
- Solve a problem using addition and multiplication by working systematically

</td><td>

Reasoning skills
- Solving problems
- Working systematically
- Spotting patterns and relationships
- Conjecturing and convincing

</td><td>

Curriculum link

1,3 Multiplication and division: prime numbers and prime factors

</td></tr>
</table>

The problem

Problem 3

Threes and fives

Joe was wondering, if you had the numbers 3 and 5 only, which numbers between 1 and 100 could you make?

For example, Yasmin noticed you could make:

- 20 by adding 5 + 5 + 5 + 5
- 9 by adding 3 + 3 + 3
- 14 by adding 5 + 3 + 3 + 3.

What other numbers could you make?

Your challenge

Work systematically to investigate which numbers it is possible to make by using the numbers 3 and 5 only. Can you find all numbers between 1 and 100 which it is possible to make?

Things to think about

- What numbers could you make using just 3 or just 5?
- Is there more than one way to make some numbers?
- How are you going to record the numbers that it is possible/isn't possible to make?
- Once you have found ways to make certain numbers, can you use this to help you make different numbers? For example, can you use the way to make 14 to help you make 28?

Year 3

Problem Solving and Reasoning

Background knowledge

- Children find all the numbers between 1 and 100 which can be made using any combination of the numbers 3 and 5.
- The results can be recorded on a 100 square (Resource sheet 3.1) to help children spot patterns and relationships.
- Children could first list all numbers which it is possible to make using just 3s or just 5s, (i.e. all multiples of 3 or 5 between 1 and 100).
- Children can then combine these multiples to make other numbers (they can only use addition, not subtraction). They will quickly realise that it is impossible to make the numbers 1, 2, 4 and 7, but they then start to use combinations of

multiples of 3 and 5 to make other numbers between 8 and 100.
- All numbers above 8 are possible to be made using a combination of 3s and 5s.
- Children should be encouraged to use numbers which they know they can create with 3s and 5s to make other numbers. For example, 16 can be partitioned into 8 + 8, so it can be made by 5 + 3 + 5 + 3 or 5 + 5 + 3 + 3; 24 can be partitioned into 8 + 8 + 8 so it can be made out of 5 + 5 + 5 + 3 + 3 + 3, etc.
- When children progress to higher numbers, you could begin to introduce the use of brackets to record calculations, e.g. 91 can be recorded as (17 × 5) + 3 + 3.

Launching the activity

1. Display a 100 square on the whiteboard (and/or provide an individual 100 square per child) and begin by asking children to 'think, pair, share' which numbers between 1 and 100 it would be possible to make by using just 5s.

2. Discuss this together, marking on all numbers which it is possible to make using just 5s on the 100 square. Establish that these numbers are all multiples of 5.

3. List the numbers on the working wall as a list of just numbers which you can make with just 5 or just 3s, (e.g. 5, 10, 15, 20 and 3, 6, 9, 12).

4. Introduce the problem by sharing the prompt problem poster with the children. Ensure children are familiar with the term 'systematically'.

5. Ask children to discuss with their partner possible ways of working on the problem, stressing the need to work systematically. Share some of these with the class.

6. Allow time for children to work in small groups on the problem. Ask children *What do you notice?* Adults should spend time with each group, scaffolding their thinking and reasoning as appropriate.

7. During the session draw the whole class's attention to specific groups that are working systematically.

8. At the end of the session bring children back together and discuss their findings and things that they have noticed.

9. End the session by challenging groups to a race to make certain numbers, e.g. *89, 126,* using just 3s and 5s.

Developing reasoning

➤ *What do you notice* about the numbers you can make using 3s and 5s? Are they all odd/even? What other properties do they share?
➤ If you know you can make 8 out of 3s and 5s, *what else do you know?*
➤ Give me a *peculiar and obvious* way to make 45 using 3s and 5s.
➤ *Convince me* that you can make all numbers above 8 using just 3s and 5s.
➤ Give me a *hard and easy* number to make by just using 3s and 5s. Why is it hard/easy?

Providing differentiation

Support
Children could first explore numbers in a restricted range (e.g. 1–30) before extending this range if they are able. Ensure that all children have access to a range of resources to help them represent the problem and record their solutions.

Extension
Children could explore ways to make a set of numbers above 100, (e.g. 346, 129, 1003), including using larger multiples of 3 and 5. Children could also be challenged to make the largest number they can using a combination of 3 and 5. Children could also explore using other pairs of numbers, (e.g. 4 and 6).

 Key strategies

3 Convince me
4 Hard and easy
8 Peculiar, obvious, general
10 What do you notice?
12 What's the same? What's different?

 Problem-solving approaches

Graffiti maths
Small group work
Think, pair, share

Taking it further

The activity could be extended into other work on multiples of number, including 4, 6 and 8 or other problems that require children to work systemically.

4 Alien farm

The problem

Alien farm (1)

We have managed to capture some aliens!

We have found two different types of aliens:

- Duo aliens who have 2 legs

- Quadro aliens who have 4 legs.

It's too dangerous to get too close to them and we've screened off most of their enclosure to protect the public, but I can see 24 legs.

How many of each type of alien could we have in our alien enclosure?

Things to think about

- If we just had Duo or Quadro aliens, how many would we have?
- What combinations of 2 and 4 make 24?

Your challenge

Work out all the possible combinations of aliens which we could have in our enclosure.

RISING STARS
Maths

Year 3   *Problem Solving and Reasoning*

Background knowledge

- This problem asks the children to work systematically to find all possible combinations.
- The children are introduced to different types of aliens – Duo aliens have 2 legs; Quadro aliens have 4 legs; Octo aliens which have 8 legs. Children are given a total number of alien legs and must work out the different combinations of each type of alien that could be present.
- Four different levels of poster are provided. Problems 4a–4d progress in difficulty, as there are more combinations possible as you move through the posters. Poster 4d introduces an additional constraint of the total number of aliens, resulting in there being only one solution which fits the criteria given in the problem.
- The numbers or pairs of legs have been set so

that they are multiples of 2, 4 and 8.
- Children need to work systematically in order to solve this problem. They could first start by working out how many aliens would be present if all aliens are Duo or Quadro.
- The children then need to work out the various combinations possible if the types of aliens are mixed. They should notice that 1 Quadro alien can be exchanged for 2 Duo aliens and 2 Duo aliens can be exchanged for 1 Quadro alien. This should lead to a systematic way of recording. For example, for problem 4a with 24 legs in total):
- For problem 4d, children will need to work in a similar way, but consider which combination of Duo and Quadro aliens gives the total stated.

Duos	Quadros
12	0
10	1
8	2
6	3
4	4
2	5
0	6

Launching the activity

1. Count in multiples of 2, 4 and then 8 and discuss relationships between these multiples.

2. Then introduce the problem by sharing the version of prompt poster which the majority of the children will be working on.

3. Ask children to 'think, pair, share.' See if they can they come up with three possible solutions.

4. Encourage children to discuss how they came up with these solutions and how they think they could extend this to find all possible solutions.

5. Ask the children how they are going to ensure that they have found all possible combinations. Discuss the importance of working systematically.

6. Provide time for children to work on the activity, ideally in threes or fours of similar abilities.

7. During the activity, draw children's attention to any good examples of systematic working.

8. At the end of the session bring children together to compare findings and ways of working.

Developing reasoning

➤ *What do you notice about the number of Duo, Quadro and Octo aliens that it is possible to have?*

➤ *What's the same? What's different about Duo, Quadro and Octo aliens? How are they linked together?*

➤ *If we know that we can have* [pick a possible solution from the children's work], *what else do we know?*

➤ *Convince me that the way you are working will mean you will find all possible solutions.*

Providing differentiation

Support
The children should focus on solving the problem in the prompt poster. A range of practical representations will help the children represent and visualise the problem.

Extension
The children should focus on problem 4c and then problem 4d, which has additional criteria to meet. They could then design their own version of problem 4d, using new aliens with different numbers of legs.

 Key strategies

2 Another, another, another
3 Convince me
10 What do you notice?
11 What else do we know?

 Problem-solving approaches

Ability groups

Taking it further

This activity will also work well alongside other problems that involve working systematically Other problems in this resource that require children to work systemically include problem 1, 2 and 3 (there are several others in the resource).

There are also additional 'alien' themed problems in this resource, e.g. problems 2, 4 and 15 are all alien themed, which could form a series of 'alien' themed lessons.

5 Number guess who

The problem

Number guess who

This is a game of 'Guess who' with a maths twist! Here's how to play. You will need a partner to play with, a copy of the same game board and something to mark your board with.

Start by both choosing a number from your board. Write this in the 'My number' box. Your partner will ask you a question to try and work out what your number is. You must answer 'yes' or 'no'.

Your partner will try to work out which numbers you can't have chosen and cross these off the board. Keep going, until your partner has worked out the number.

Things to think about

- Does it matter which number you choose as your number?
- What questions can you ask that allow you to cross off the most numbers and get closer to your partner's chosen number?
- Can you think of any questions that do not involve place value, e.g. **not like** 'Does your number have a 3 in the hundreds place?'

Your challenge

Play the game, thinking of different strategies you could use to win.

Background knowledge

- This investigation takes the form of a game, based on the popular children's game 'Guess who'.
- Children have to ask questions to identify the number that their partner has selected from their game board.
- Each place in a number is named as follows:

Th	H	T	O
|	|	|	|
Thousands	Hundreds	Tens	Ones

- There are three versions of the game board provided (Resource sheets 5.1, 5.2 and 5.3). Board 1 involves ThHTO and HTO numbers, Board 2 involves HTO numbers and Board 3 involves ThHTO numbers and is intended as an extension.

- All the boards have a range of numbers on them, which require careful questioning in order to differentiate between. However, on each board there is at least one number which, if chosen, could be identified by using a single question.
- Numbers lines, both marked and blank, are an effective resource to help children understand the concept place value. Gattegno charts (place value charts) can also be used effectively.

Launching the activity

1. Begin by selecting six numbers from Resource sheet 5.1 (that the majority of the class will be using) and display these on the board.

2. Pick one of the numbers and write it down on a piece of paper, unseen by the children.

3. Ask the children to 'think, pair, share' some 'yes/no' questions that they could ask you to help them work out which of the numbers you have selected.

4. Allow the children to ask you the questions, until they have established which number you have chosen. You may wish to discuss the effectiveness of each question and how they could be improved. They could ask for example, *Does your number have a nine in the tens place?* or *Is your number bigger than 1000?*

5. Share the prompt poster. Read through the rules together and ask any questions.

6. Give the children time to play the game in similar ability pairs.

7. Once most children have finished a game, bring the class back together. Discuss the questions they have been asking their partners to try and establish what numbers they have selected. Discuss how these could be refined and ask them now to focus on strategies to 'win'. What numbers should they select as their number? What questions should they ask in order to eliminate numbers? At this point also try to encourage children to not ask repeated place value related questions, but to explore other questions they could ask in order to eliminate numbers.

8. At the end of the session, bring the children back together and discuss the 'winning strategies' they developed.

Developing reasoning

➤ *What do you notice* about the value of the [7] in this number compared to this number?
➤ *What's the same What's different* between [pick two or more numbers from the game board]?
➤ Give me a **hard and easy** number for your partner to guess.
➤ Give me a number **Another, another, another.** [with 6 in its ones column]/[higher than 400].
➤ Which number from the grid is the **odd one out** and why?

Providing differentiation

Support
Children should work from Resource sheet 5.2, which only requires knowledge of place value up to HTO. Children will also benefit from access to some of the practical resources mentioned in the 'background knowledge' section.

Extension
Resource sheet 5.3 (up to ThHTO) introduces children to place value up to Ten Thousandths value. Further restrictions can also be placed on the questions that children can ask, e.g. don't mention the value of the hundreds digit, only ask questions that compare the number to another number, etc.

 Key strategies

2 Another, another, another
4 Hard and easy
7 Odd one out
10 What do you notice?
12 What's the same? What's different?

 Problem-solving approaches

Paired work
Think, pair, share

Taking it further

Children could create their own number 'Guess who' boards that lead to the longest game possible, e.g. similar numbers, multiple possible options, etc.

The place value 'Guess who' boards can also be used as a 'zooming in' board (see Key strategy 13) or as the basis for an ordering activity.

6 Missing problems

Learning objective
- Create word problems using a range of different situations.

Reasoning skills
- Solving problems
- Making connections
- Reasoning numerical

Curriculum link
1,3 Addition and subtraction, Multi-step problems

The problem

Missing problems

In today's lesson I was going to ask you to solve lots of different worded problems, but you'll never believe this: my cat put muddy paw prints all over my problems!

So, can you help me re-create the word problems?

I remember that there were eight problems.

- At least two of the problems involve multi-steps.

- At least two of the problems involve multi-operations.

- One of the problems involved fractions.

- One of the problems involved measures.

- One of the problems involved scaling, e.g. something was four times as a high as …

Your challenge

Create word problems meeting the criteria above.

Things to think about

- What type of situations do we use maths in?
- What type of situations could your word problems involve?
- How are you going to make sure your problem is solvable?

RISING STARS
Maths

Year 3   Problem Solving and Reasoning

Background knowledge

- This problem asks children to write their own word problems for a range of different contexts.
- Children's responses and the problems they choose to create during this session will provide a clear indication of their level of confidence with the application of addition, subtraction, multiplication and division.
- The children are asked to create a range of different problems that fulfil set criteria:
  - *Multi-step problems*, e.g. having to carry out more than one calculation, such as a question that involves multiplication and addition.
  - *Multi-operation problems*, e.g. a question which involved division and then

  subtraction. All multi-operation problems will also be multi-step problems.
  - *Fraction problems*, e.g. finding a simple fraction of a number in context.
  - *Measures problems*, e.g. calculating the total weight or calculating the perimeter.
  - *Scaling problems* which connect one value to another, e.g. Brodie was three times taller than his son Josh who, was 65 cm tall. How tall is Brodie?
- All the criteria above are taken from the Year 3 programme of study.
- Children should be encouraged to use a range of real-life contexts for their problems, e.g. measurements, money, survey responses, etc.

Launching the activity

1. Introduce the prompt poster. Adding extra 'drama' is encouraged, but optional!

2. Begin by asking the children to think about when they may use maths in 'real life'. Gradually snowball these suggestions together, to create a shared list on the interactive whiteboard or working wall.

3. Model the creation of a worded problem together with the children. Focus on the language used when writing the problem in order to support the children to use appropriate language when writing their own problems.

4. Give the children time create their problems, preferably working in pairs in order to encourage discussion.

5. Then ask the children to switch their problems with another pair and give them time to solve each other's worded problems. They can make each other's word problems more complex, e.g. by adding a step, adding in fractions, etc.

6. At the end of the session discuss the different types of problems created. Which problems were hard or easy to solve? Which problems were the most realistic?

Developing reasoning

➤ *Give me a situation where you would use maths in real life.* **Another, another, another.**
➤ *Give me a* **hard and easy** *word problem. What makes it hard/easy?*
➤ **What's the same. What's different** *between these two problems which you have created?*
➤ **Convince me** *that this problem is solvable.*
➤ *Give me a* **silly answer** *to this problem you have written. What makes it silly?*

Providing differentiation

Support
Children should focus initially on creating single step problems. Children may also benefit from being provided with the base calculation on which to build a worded problem around, e.g. 8 × 5 = 40.

Extension
Children could be challenged to ensure that each of their problems which they create has a different underlying structure and relies on a different combination of operations. Children could also be encouraged to create more problems which involve fractions and proportionality.

 Key strategies

2 Another, another, another
3 Convince me
4 Hard and easy
9 Silly answers
12 What's the same? What's different?

 Problem-solving approaches

Paired work
Think, pair, share

Taking it further

The activity could be used as a springboard to discuss effective strategies to solve worded problems and creating problems to specific criteria, e.g. it has to be about money, involve the fraction $\frac{1}{4}$ and involve two steps.

Learning objective
• Problem solve using place value in numbers up to 1000.

Reasoning skills
• Solving problems
• Making connections
• Working systematically
• Conjecturing and convincing

Curriculum link
1₂3 Properties of number: place value

The problem

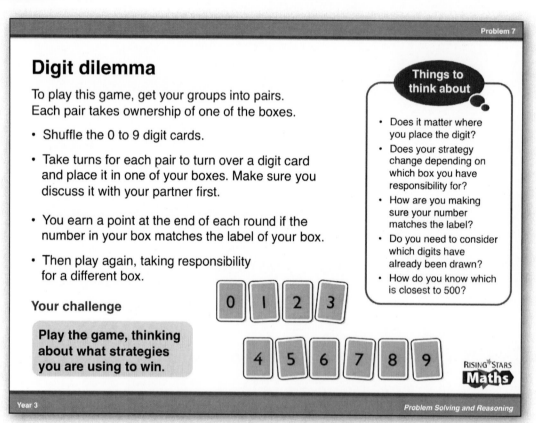

Problem 7

Digit dilemma

To play this game, get your groups into pairs. Each pair takes ownership of one of the boxes.

• Shuffle the 0 to 9 digit cards.

• Take turns for each pair to turn over a digit card and place it in one of your boxes. Make sure you discuss it with your partner first.

• You earn a point at the end of each round if the number in your box matches the label of your box.

• Then play again, taking responsibility for a different box.

Your challenge

Play the game, thinking about what strategies you are using to win.

Things to think about

• Does it matter where you place the digit?
• Does your strategy change depending on which box you have responsibility for?
• How are you making sure your number matches the label?
• Do you need to consider which digits have already been drawn?
• How do you know which is closest to 500?

0 1 2 3

4 5 6 7 8 9

RISING STARS Maths

Year 3

Problem Solving and Reasoning

Background knowledge

• This problem takes the form of a competitive game, which children play in groups of three pairs (6 children in each group).

• Children are given a game board with a set of HTO place holders and the labels *'Lowest'*, *'Closest to 500'* and *'Highest'* (Resource sheet 7.1). Each pair takes responsibility for a set of place holders and their aim is to make sure that, at the end of each round, their number meets the label assigned to it.

• Each pair of children are given a set of 0–9 digit cards (Resource sheet 7.2) and they generate digits by turning over one of the cards.

• Once the children have placed the digit card, they cannot move it. It also obviously cannot be drawn again this round.

• Children will need to reason about the best place for them to place each digit they have generated and discuss each digit placement together with their partner, convincing each other of the best place to place each digit.

• Through discussion, the children should be encouraged to consider the best 'strategy' in order to give the best chance of creating a number which conforms to each of the labels.

• Children will, of course, have to consider the place value that each digit 'attracts' when they are placed in different places in the number.

Launching the activity

1. Begin by modelling a version of this game with the class. You could play class vs. teacher or split the class in half. Write up three place holders for each 'team' on the board.

   ___ ___ ___

2. Explain that the aim of the game is to create the biggest number possible. Each team will take it in turns turn over a digit card and they need to place the digit in one of their place holders.

3. Play this version of the game together, repeating as necessary.

4. Ask the children to 'think, pair, share' with a partner what strategies they could use for this game. Discuss these together as a class, ensuring that place value is discussed.

5. Explain that they are going to be playing a different version of this game together and introduce the game using the prompt poster.

6. Model the playing of this game, with the teacher playing against two sets of pairs of children. The teacher should verbalise their thoughts and reasoning, modelling the reasoning expected during the activity.

7. Allow plenty of time for children to explore the problem and play the game numerous times. Stress that children should be thinking about 'strategies', about how they can give themselves the best chance of winning and how they differ depending on the goal.

8. At the end of the session, bring the children back together and ask each group to share one of the rules they have been using in order to stand the greatest chance of completing the challenge.

Developing reasoning

➤ ***What do you notice*** about the value of the [3] *when placed here or here?*

➤ ***What's the same. What's different*** *between placing [3] in this number?*

➤ *Give me a* **hard and easy** *digit to place. Why is this hard or easy?*

➤ *Are the strategies you use the same for each label?*

➤ *Give me a* **silly place** *to place this digit. Why is it a silly place to place it?*

Providing differentiation

Support
Children could focus initially on the basic game modelled at the start of shared learning. A Gattegno chart and place value cards may also be useful to support children with the place value element of this activity. Children could also play in their pairs on just two of the three sets of boxes, e.g. highest and lowest.

Extension
Children could use Resource sheet 7.3, a game board with ThHTO place holders. They should be encouraged to create winning strategies for each box label.

 Key strategies

3 Convince me
9 Silly answers
11 What else do we know?
12 What's the same? What's different?

 Problem-solving approaches

Small-group work

Taking it further

The rules of this activity can be tweaked in order to create a different game:

- Create a 'nasty' version of the game by placing the digit card in any space on the game board.
- A 'nice' version of the game where children have to work together to ensure that all three labels are true.
- Replace digit cards with a ten sided 0–9 dice, or a 0–9 spinner, which adds in an extra element of uncertainty, as it is now possible to generate the same digit more than once.

8 Fabulous 28

Learning objective
- Investigate properties of and patterns in numbers.

Reasoning skills
- Making connections
- Working systematically
- Finding all possibilities

Curriculum link
- Properties of number:
  Addition and subtraction
  Multiplication and division
  Proportionality

The problem

Fabulous 28

Today, my favourite number is 28. I wonder how many different statements and/or questions we could write that have the answer 28?

Some challenges to try:
- Write five questions that also involve the number 60.
- Write some questions in a context.
- Write some statements that involve two different operations.
- Write some statements that involve a fraction.

Things to think about

- Can you use any patterns to help you?
- Is there an infinite number of questions and statements which have the answer 28?
- Do you know any properties that the number 28 has?

Your challenge

Create as many different statements and/or questions as you can with the answer 28.

28 28
28 28
28
28

RISING STARS
Maths

Year 3

Problem Solving and Reasoning

Background knowledge

- This problem asks the children to investigate the number 28, by generating as many different possible questions or statements to which the 'answer' is 28.
- This is a combination and extension of the 'If this is the answer, what is the question?' and 'Maths stories' key strategies, so these sections may be useful to read before leading this activity.
- Children should be encouraged to spot and continue patterns in order to create related questions/statements easily, e.g.
  o $1 \times 28 = 28$
  o $2 \times 14 = 28$
  o $4 \times 7 = 28$
  o $8 \times 3.5 = 28$

- On the prompt poster some suggested challenge questions are provided. Similar prompt questions can be created by the teacher as needed. Children can also be encouraged to set each other challenges.
- Children should be encouraged to make a wide range of statements, which involve many areas of mathematics. Combined with focused questioning, this activity can therefore provide a very good opportunity for assessment of a wide range of different areas of mathematics.

Launching the activity

1. Begin by showing the number 28 on the board. Give children two minutes to write down as many different things that they know about 28 as they can (see key strategy, Maths stories).

2. In pairs ask the children to compare their 'stories'. Have they all written similar things?

3. Share some statements from the children's 'stories' as a class, recording them on the board and/or working wall.

4. Share the prompt poster with the children. Provide a brief time for children to discuss the prompt poster together.

5. Allow children the majority of the session to work in mixed-ability groups (of three or four in each group) on this challenge. Stress that all children in the group must understand a statement/question before it is written down.

6. Whilst children are working provide further prompt/challenge questions in order to further develop their thinking and reasoning.

7. Towards the end of the session bring the children back together and ask each group to share a peculiar and obvious statement/question which they have written, and explain why this is peculiar/obvious.

Developing reasoning

➤ *What do you notice* about the number 28?
➤ Give me a *hard and easy* statement/question that has the answer 28.
➤ Give me a *peculiar and obvious* statement/question?
➤ Can you give a related statement/question to this one? How are they related? *Another, another, another.*

➤ Give me a *silly statement* that clearly isn't related to 28. Why is it silly?
➤ If we know that [pick statement made by the children], *what else do we know*?

Providing differentiation

Support
Woking in mixed-ability groups, as suggested above, should provide peer support for less confident children. The children could also be encouraged to continue simple patterns, e.g. with the statements $2 + 26 = 28$, $3 + 25 = 28$, $4 + 24 = 28$.

Extension
The children should be given increasingly more complex challenge questions, e.g. *Can you give me a statement which involves a number less than one? Can you give me a question/statement which has more than three numbers in it?*

 Key strategies

3   Convince me
4   Hard and easy
8   Peculiar, obvious, general
9   Silly answers
10 What do you notice?
11 What else do we know?
12 What's the same? What's different?

 Problem-solving approaches

Mixed-ability groups
Graffiti maths

Taking it further

The activity can easily be extended to other numbers and mathematical concepts. See the Key strategy sections for more ideas.

The activity can also be developed by giving different groups a different number to work on, e.g. 28, 30, 48, and asking children to convince the class that their number is the most 'special'.

9 Remainder, remainder

<table>
<tr>
<td>

Learning objective
• Investigate patterns in division.

</td>
<td>

Reasoning skills
• Making generalisations
• Spotting patterns and relationships
• Finding all possibilities
• Making connections

</td>
<td>

Curriculum link
1 2 3 Multiplication and division: remainders

</td>
</tr>
</table>

The problem

Problem 9a

Remainder, remainder (1)

I've been thinking about division and which division sentences result in remainders.

Are there any patterns, or rules, that would allow us to predict the remainder for a calculation without necessarily carrying it out in full?

Can you work out:

• Which numbers between 1 and 30 would have a remainder of 1 when divided by 3?

• Which numbers between 1 and 40 would have a remainder of 2 when divided by 4?

• Which numbers between 1 and 60 would have a remainder of 4 when divided by 6?

Things to think about

• What does a remainder mean?
• Which type of calculations result in remainders?
• How are multiplication and division related to each other?

Your challenge

Investigate the questions above and create rules to help you work out the remainder. Once you have done this, can you create your own statements to investigate and find rules for?

Year 3

Problem Solving and Reasoning

Background knowledge

• This activity asks children to investigate which numbers within a given range will give certain remainders when divided by a given number, e.g. *which numbers between 1 and 40 will give a remainder of 2 when divided by 4?*

• Two versions of the problem are provided, with version 2 being slightly more challenging and having more possible solutions than version 1.

• Children will need to demonstrate a true conceptual understanding of division. They need to recognise that division can be thought of as both grouping and sharing and that remainders arise when there are things 'left over' after dividing. The remainder can never be greater than the number you are dividing by.

• Practical representations and resources, such as counters, cubes and number lines will assist the children in visualising the structure of division and why remainders occur. Children could also shade or colour the numbers on a 100 square to see patterns.

• Children will also need to use their knowledge of the inverse relationship between multiplication and division in order to make generalisations to efficiently solve this problem.

• Numbers have remainders when they are the distance of the remainder away from a multiple of the number being divided by. For example, all numbers which are 2 more than a multiple of 4 have a remainder of 2 when divided by 4; all numbers which are 5 more than a multiple of 6 have a remainder of 5 when divided by 6.

Launching the activity

1. Begin displaying the words 'Division' and 'Remainder' on a whiteboard and ask the children to 'think, pair, share' a definition for both of these words. Discuss this together, creating a shared definition of both words. Depending on your class you may need to spend more time here exploring (using practical resources) that division can be seen as both grouping and sharing.

2. Introduce the prompt poster. In pairs, give children time to initially discuss the prompt poster, considering how they could approach the problem and their initial conjectures. Discuss children's initial thoughts/conjectures and record these on the whiteboard or working wall.

3. Provide time for children to work on the activity, ideally working in pairs to encourage discussion and develop reasoning.

4. Give support as needed, developing their reasoning and ability to make connections, and generalisations.

5. Finish the lesson by discussing the different results children have found and ways they have used to work out their results. Finally, discuss any generalisations that children, either as pairs or the whole class, could make about how you could find numbers that would have any specific remainder when divided by a certain number.

Developing reasoning

➤ *Give me a number that would have a remainder of [2] when divided by [4].* ***Another, another, another.***

➤ ***What's the same. What's different*** *between the numbers which have a remainder of [2] when divided by [4]? /between multiplication and division.*

➤ *Give me a* ***silly answer*** *for a number that will have a remainder of [1] when divided by [3]. Why is it silly?*

➤ *If you know that [28] has a remainder of [1] when divided by [3],* ***what else do we know?***

➤ ***Convince me*** *that this number will have a remainder of [1] when divided by [3]?*

Providing differentiation

Support

Children should focus on the problem 9a, which can be adapted to involve division and multiplication facts which they are familiar with. Access to a range of familiar representations to represent this problem will also be beneficial for all children, especially those who require more support. Alternatively, the book, *A Remainder of One* by Ellnor J Pinczes, which looks at dividing 25 by different numbers until there is no remainder, could be explored by the children.

Extension

Children should be encouraged to use what they have found from working on problem 9b to create generalised statements about finding numbers with set remainders when divided by any given number. They should use this generalisation to make and investigate their own similar statements.

 Key strategies

2 Another, another, another
3 Convince me
9 Silly answers
10 What do you notice?
12 What's the same? What's different?

 Problem-solving approaches

Paired work

Taking it further

Children could explore other times tables, such as the 8 times table, and linked tables such as the 12 times table (double 6 times table).

Learning objective
- Investigate fractions which are equal to each other.

Reasoning skills
- Solving problems
- Making connections
- Working systematically
- Conjecturing and convincing

Curriculum link
 Fractions: proportionality

The problem

Build a wall

Your teacher will give you some strips of paper.

Fold the strips so that the strips show:

- 1 whole, $\frac{1}{2}$, $\frac{1}{4}$, $\frac{1}{3}$, $\frac{1}{6}$ and $\frac{1}{8}$.

Put them underneath each other, so that they are all lined up.

Can you use the fraction wall which you have just created to work out which fractions are equal (equivalent) to each other?

Your challenge

Create a fraction wall and use it to help find fractions that are equal to each other.

Extra challenge
Can you work out how to find fractions that are equal to each other without using the fraction wall?

> **Things to think about**
>
> - What does a fraction actually mean?
> - How can you fold your strips to show each fraction?
> - How are the different fractions related to each other?
> - What's the same and what's different between pairs of fractions that are equivalent?

RISING STARS
Maths

Year 3 — Problem Solving and Reasoning

Problem 10

Background knowledge

- This activity asks the children to fold strips to represent different fractions, in order to create their own fraction wall. Children are then encouraged to use these to make statements about fractions which are equivalent to each other.
- In order to do this, children will need to understand that:
  o Fractions represent a proportion.
  o A fraction is made up of two parts: a numerator and a denominator.
  o The denominator shows how many equal parts the whole is split into.
  o The numerator shows how many of these equal parts are represented/'needed'.

- The children need six equal sized strips. The strips are formed by cutting an A4 sheet of paper into strips of paper. Four strips cut length ways are ideal for this activity. (Resource sheet 10.1 can also be used.)
- Children can use the strips folded into $\frac{1}{4}$s to help create $\frac{1}{8}$s and $\frac{1}{3}$s to help create $\frac{1}{6}$s.
- Fractions are equivalent to each other when the numerator and denominator are linked by a common scale factor, e.g. $\frac{1}{4}$ and $\frac{3}{12}$ are equivalent as they are linked by a scale factor of 3.

Launching the activity

1. Show the word 'Fraction' on the whiteboard. Ask the children to 'think, pair, share'. *What does the word 'fraction' mean?* Discuss this together, drawing out that a fraction is a way of showing a proportion.

2. Share the prompt poster with the children.

3. Give the children time to fold the strips to show the fractions on the poster. Working in pairs facilitate a discussion and their reasoning.

4. Once the children have created all of their fractions strips, ask how these could be assembled to form a fraction wall and photograph different arrangements.

5. Ask children to 'think, pair, share'. How could the fraction wall be used to help find fractions which are equal to each other?

6. Take some children's suggestions of equivalent fractions, recording them on the whiteboard or working wall.

7. Provide time for the children to use their fraction walls to write down fractions which are equivalent to each other. Discuss the usefulness of different arrangements of the fraction wall.

8. Once children have found equivalent fractions using the fraction wall, ask them to consider what's the same? and what's different? between fractions that are equivalent to each other. Allow time for children to consider this and if possible create equivalent fraction statements that are not taken from the fraction wall.

9. At the end of the session, ask the children to share what they have noticed and how they can find equivalent fractions.

Developing reasoning

➤ *If we know that ($\frac{1}{2}$ and $\frac{2}{4}$ are equivalent)* **what else do we know?**

➤ **What's the same, what's different** *between these two equivalent fractions?*

➤ **Convince me** *that these fractions are equal to each other.*

➤ *Which of these fractions is the* **odd one out** *and why?*

➤ *Give me a* **silly answer** *for a fraction that is equal to ($\frac{1}{4}$). What makes it silly?*

➤ *Give a fraction that is equal to ($\frac{1}{4}$)* **another, another and another.**

Providing differentiation

Support

Children should focus on folding strips to show $\frac{1}{2}$, $\frac{1}{4}$ and $\frac{1}{8}$, and create equivalency statements using these. The children may also find the printed fraction wall (Resource sheet 10.2) useful if they struggle to fold the strips to represent the different fractions.

Extension

Children should be encouraged to undertake a greater proportion of the challenge independently.

 Key strategies

2 Another, another, another
3 Convince me
9 Silly answers
11 What else do we know?
12 What's the same? What's different?

 Problem-solving approaches

Paired work
Think, pair, share

Taking it further

The activity could be used as a springboard for further work on fractions, including representations of fractions (see problem 11) or fractions of amounts (see problem 12). Children could also use their fraction wall to explore the addition of fractions.

11 Fraction pictures

Learning objective
- Explore different representations for fractions.

Reasoning skills
- Making connections
- Exploring representations

Curriculum link
$\frac{1}{2}$ Fractions: proportionality

The problem

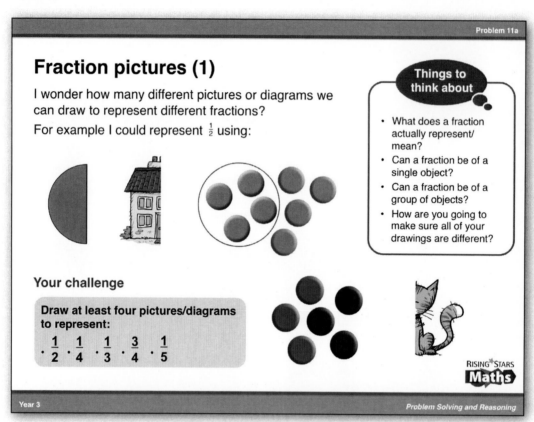

Problem 11a

Fraction pictures (1)

I wonder how many different pictures or diagrams we can draw to represent different fractions?

For example I could represent $\frac{1}{2}$ using:

Things to think about

- What does a fraction actually represent/ mean?
- Can a fraction be of a single object?
- Can a fraction be of a group of objects?
- How are you going to make sure all of your drawings are different?

Your challenge

Draw at least four pictures/diagrams to represent:

$\frac{1}{2}$. $\frac{1}{4}$. $\frac{1}{3}$. $\frac{3}{4}$. $\frac{1}{5}$

RISING STARS
Maths

Year 3   Problem Solving and Reasoning

Background knowledge

- This problem asks the children to explore different ways of representing fractions.
- There are two versions of the prompt provided, with problem 11b focusing on fractions where the numerator is greater than 1.
- Through this activity you will be able to gain an accurate assessment of children's conceptual understanding of fractions.
- Fractions are one way of representing a proportion. This can be a proportion of anything including a set of objects, of a number or a single object/number.
- A fraction is made up of two parts – a numerator and a denominator.

  numerator — $\frac{1}{3}$ — denominator

- The denominator shows how many equal parts the whole is split into.
- The numerator shows how many of these equal parts are represented/'needed'.
- Children should be encouraged to show a range of different representations of a fraction during this activity including:
  o Representations showing fractions of a range of shapes.
  o Representations showing fractions of objects - where the number of objects matches the denominator.
  o Representations showing fractions of objects - where the number of objects does not match the denominator.

Launching the activity

1. Show the word 'fraction' on the whiteboard. Ask the children to 'think, pair, share.' What does the word fraction' mean?

2. Discuss this together, drawing out that a fraction is a way of showing a proportion.

3. Show the fraction $\frac{1}{2}$ on the whiteboard. Ask children to identify the name and meaning of the top and bottom number of the fraction.

4. Working on paper or mini whiteboards, ask the children to draw you a way to show $\frac{1}{2}$. Then ask them for **another, another** and **another** way of showing $\frac{1}{2}$. Ask the children to compare their four representations with a partner and discuss what's the same? what's different? between the representations that they have drawn.

5. Share the prompt poster with children. Give them time to work on the problem. This can either be individually (which will allow for close assessment of each child's conceptual understanding) or in pairs/small groups (which will allow for greater discussion and reasoning).

6. Whilst the children are working on the problem, challenge them to create different representations, e.g. *Next, show me a representation that does not involve a square/circle.*

7. At the end of the session ask children to compare their representations with a partner and consider what's the same? what's different? between the representations.

8. Finally, ask the children to select their most peculiar representation of a fraction and explain why it is peculiar.

Developing reasoning

➤ Give me a **hard and easy** way of representing [fraction]. *What makes it heard/easy?*

➤ ***What's the same. What's different*** *between these two different representations?*

➤ ***Convince me*** *that this is a representation of* [fraction].

➤ *Which of your representations is the **odd one out** and why?*

➤ *Give me a **peculiar, obvious** and **general** representation for* [fraction].

Providing differentiation

Support
Children should focus initially on representing fractions where the numerator is one. A range of practical resources will also help children create physical representations, before transferring these to drawn representations/diagrams.

Extension
Children could be challenged to ensure that each of their representations are unique. They could also be challenged to create more complex representations, e.g. representing $\frac{5}{6}$ of three circles.

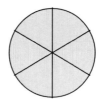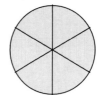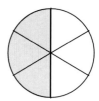

 Key strategies

3 Convince me
4 Hard and easy
7 Odd one out
8 Peculiar, obvious, general
12 What's the same? What's different?

Problem-solving approaches

Paired work
Think, pair, share

Taking it further

The activity could be used as a springboard to further work on fractions, including equivalent fractions (see problem 9) or fractions of amounts (see problem 11).

<table>
</table>

Learning objective	Reasoning skills	Curriculum link
• Solve problems involving finding fractions of amounts.	• Solving problems • Making connections • Working systematically	$\frac{1}{2}$ Fractions: proportions and money

The problem

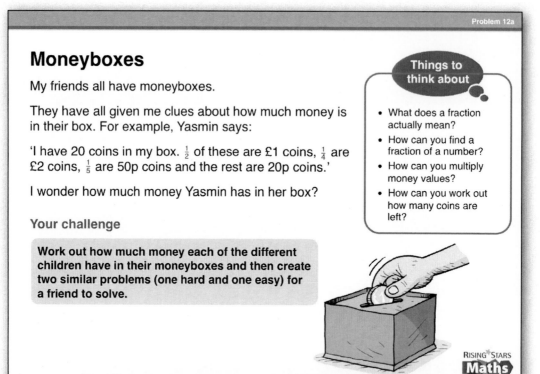

Problem 12a

Moneyboxes

My friends all have moneyboxes.

They have all given me clues about how much money is in their box. For example, Yasmin says:

'I have 20 coins in my box. $\frac{1}{2}$ of these are £1 coins, $\frac{1}{4}$ are £2 coins, $\frac{1}{5}$ are 50p coins and the rest are 20p coins.'

I wonder how much money Yasmin has in her box?

Your challenge

Work out how much money each of the different children have in their moneyboxes and then create two similar problems (one hard and one easy) for a friend to solve.

Things to think about

• What does a fraction actually mean?
• How can you find a fraction of a number?
• How can you multiply money values?
• How can you work out how many coins are left?

Year 3

RISING STARS
Maths

Problem Solving and Reasoning

Background knowledge

- This problem asks the children to calculate fractions of a quantity and combine this with their knowledge of money in order to work out the total amount present in a moneybox.
- They are told the total number of coins in a moneybox, then given a number of clues to help them to work out the total value of the coins.
- In order to calculate fractions of quantities, children need to understand that:
  o Fractions represent a proportion.
  o A fraction is made up of two parts – a numerator and a denominator.
  o The denominator shows how many equal parts the whole is split into.
  o The numerator shows how many of these equal parts are represented/'needed'.
- Children need to work systematically through

each problem in order to work out the number of each different value coin and therefore the total value of the coin in the moneybox.
- For example, in problem 3 (*I have 60 coins in my moneybox. $\frac{3}{4}$ of these are 50p coins, $\frac{1}{6}$ are £1 coins, there are two £2 coins and the rest are 20p coins.*), children should work out that 45 coins (60 ÷ 4 = 15, 15 × 3 = 45) are 50p coins and have a value of £22.50; ten coins are £1 coins with a value of £10; two coins are £2 coins with a value of £4. There are then three coins left (60 - 45 - 10 - 2 = 3) with a value of 60p, giving the total amount in the money box as £22.50 + £10 + £4 + 60p = £37.10.
- Five different problems are provided, which progress in difficulty. Problems 3 and above require children to calculate fractions of amounts when the numerator is greater than 1.

Launching the activity

1. Show the word 'fraction' on the whiteboard. Ask the children to 'think, pair, share.' What does the word 'fraction' mean?

2. Discuss this together, drawing out that a fraction is a way of showing a proportion.

3. Ask children to find $\frac{1}{2}$ and $\frac{3}{4}$ of 20.

4. Ask children to discuss with their partner the methods they have used. Share these as a class, modelling how to find fractions of amounts.

5. Share the poster problem with the children and give them time to work on it with a partner.

6. Discuss different children's solutions and methods together, resulting in a model of how to solve the problem on the interactive whiteboard.

7. Allow time for children to work on the problem, selecting the appropriate one for each child.

8. At the end of the session ask children to switch their hard and easy problems with a partner for each other to solve. Discuss together what made the problems hard or easy.

Developing reasoning

➤ If we know that [$\frac{1}{2}$ of the coins are £1] **what else do we know?**

➤ Which of these clues are **hard and easy** to solve? Why?

➤ **What's the same? what's different** between these two different representations?

➤ **Convince me** that this is the correct answer? That there are [5] [£1] coins in this moneybox?

➤ Give me a **silly answer** for this problem. What makes it silly?

Providing differentiation

Support
Children should focus on the first two problems, which involve fractions with a numerator of 1. Using coins to represent the problem will also be helpful.

Extension
Children could be challenged to complete the problems, which involve multiple fractions where the numerator is greater than 1. Children can also spend a longer period of time on the 'creation' element of this task.

Key strategies

3 Convince me
4 Hard and easy
9 Silly answers
11 What else do we know?
12 What's the same? What's different?

Problem-solving approaches

Paired work
Think, pair, share

Taking it further

The activity could be used as a springboard to further work on fractions, including equivalent fractions (see problem 9) or representations of fractions (see problem 10).

School trip

Learning objective
- Work systematically to solve problems involving time durations.

Reasoning skills
- Working systematically
- Finding all possibilities
- Making connections

Curriculum link
📊 Measures: time

The problem

Problem 13a

School trip

Imagine you are planning a school trip to a local medieval castle.

- We want the total cost of the trip to be no more than £11.00 per child.

- I know we need to leave school at 9:00 a.m. and be back for 3:30 p.m.

- It takes 30 minutes to travel each way and we must do at least three different things.

Look at the list of things we could do, their cost and time. I wonder how many different ways there are to spend the day at the castle?

Things to think about

- Which things in the day can't you change?
- How long do you have?
- Can you exchange some activities for others?

Your challenge

Plan as many different ways of spending the day at the castle as you can.

RISING STARS
Maths

Year 3 · *Problem Solving and Reasoning*

Background knowledge

- This activity involves children calculating with and comparing time intervals, alongside calculations involving simple amounts of money.
- Children are provided with a set of different activities (Resource sheet 13.1) which they could undertake on a medieval themed trip to a castle. Each activity has a time period associated with it. These time periods have been planned so that they are exchangeable, e.g. a medieval pottery activity (70 minutes)

could be exchanged for medieval painting (50 minutes) and medieval artefact handling (15 minutes).
- Alongside the time periods, each activity also has a cost associated to it. The children are challenged to create a timetable for the school trip that costs under £11.00 per child and fits within the timeframe 9:00 a.m.–3:30 p.m.
- The children should be secure in the knowledge that there are 60 minutes in an hour in order to carry out this activity.

Launching the activity

1. Begin by asking the children what's the same? What's different? between 60 minutes and 1 hour. Through the discussion that follows establish that there are 60 minutes in 1 hour.

2. Introduce the prompt poster 13a to the children and share the list of activities with the children. Give children time to initially discuss the problem with their partner, considering how they could approach the problem.

3. Ask: *'How long do we have for the school trip?'* and *'How long do we have at the castle?'*

4. Discuss with the children what things they **must** include in their timetable (travel and lunch).

5. Provide time for children to work on the activity, ideally working in pairs to encourage discussion and develop reasoning.

6. Once children have developed one plan for the day, ask them to develop 'another another, another' encouraging them to use the relationships between the different time periods and costs of the activities to easily create alternative plans.

7. Towards the end of the activity, ask pairs to compare their different plans for the day. What's the same? What's different?

8. Finally, discuss the different methods children have used, drawing attention to relationships and 'exchanges' possible between the different durations of the activities.

Developing reasoning

➤ *What do you notice about the durations of these activities?*
➤ *What's the same, what's different about the duration of [x] and [y]/about these two plans for the day?*

➤ *Give me a possible plan for the day. **Another, another, another**.*
➤ *Give me a **silly answer** for the plan for the day? Why is it silly?*
➤ ***Zooming in.** Give me a plan for the day which includes ... a packed lunch ... and handling medieval artefacts ... and medieval dress up ...*
➤ ***Convince me** that you have met both the cost and time criteria.*

Providing differentiation

Support
Children who are struggling with the combination of the duration and cost element could use problem 13b and Resource sheet 13.2, which removes the cost element, to focus on time durations.

Extension
Children should be encouraged to find as many related plans as possible, using the relationships between the different durations of events and costs which other schools could choose from.

Key strategies

2 Another, another, another
3 Convince me
9 Silly answers
10 What do you notice?
12 What's the same? What's different?
13 Zooming in

Problem-solving approaches

Paired work

Taking it further

This activity could be used as the springboard into further work around planning a school trip, including working out the number of buses needed, the total cost of the trip and the potential for some statistics work around children's preferred trips/activities, etc.

This activity also works well alongside problems that involve calculating with money as well as those which involve working systematically, for example problems 1 and 2 (there are others in the resource).

14 Mystery shapes

Learning objective	**Reasoning skills**	**Curriculum link**
• Understand and use properties of shapes.	• Solving problems • Using accurate language (new skills) • Communicating with others (new skills)	Geometry: properties of shapes

The problem

Mystery shapes

You will need:

• a set of mystery shape cards

• a ruler and pencil

• a partner.

Sit back-to-back with your partner. Take it in turns to take a mystery shape card and describe the shape to your partner, so that they are able to make an accurate drawing of it.

You can't tell your partner the name of the shape, e.g. you couldn't say it's a square, or it's a triangle.

Things to think about

• Which part of the shape is best to describe first?
• What properties of the shapes can you use to help describe it to your partner?
• How can you make accurate measurements?

Your challenge

Play the game with your partner, thinking of the different shape properties you could use to describe the shape.

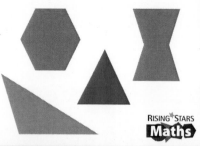

RISING STARS
Maths

Year 3

Problem Solving and Reasoning

Background knowledge

- This investigation asks children to describe shapes to a partner and encourages them to use a range of different properties of shape. Children must make an accurate drawing of their partners shape (including side lengths).
- Resource sheets 14.1 and 14.2, Mystery shapes are provided for this activity. Each shape on the sheets has whole unit length sides to assist in the measuring and reproduction of the shapes by the children.
- The children are not able to say the shape name at any point during the activity.

- Instead children need to describe the shape based on its properties. Properties of shapes that children in Year 3 should be able to use in order to describe the shape include:
  o Parallel lines/sides – two lines that have the same distance between them and will never meet.
  o Perpendicular lines/sides – two lines that meet at a right angle.
  o Right angle – a 90 degree angle.
  o Acute angles – angles smaller than a right angle.
  o Obtuse angles – angles bigger than a right angle, but smaller than a straight line.
  o Side lengths and equal length sides.

Launching the activity

1. Display the starter shape from prompt poster 14b on the interactive whiteboard. Ask the children to 'think, pair, share.' *How could we describe this shape based on its properties?*

2. Share some of the children's descriptions, taking a note of any shape properties used to make a list of terms.

3. Display this list of shape properties children have used during their description of the starter shape and add in any missing terms from the background knowledge section. Ask children to work with a partner to create a definition of each of these terms.

4. Share the children's definitions together, recording them on the whiteboard/working wall, to create a shared definition bank.

5. Also explore together any other words that could be useful to describe a shape, e.g. 'top', 'base', 'tall', 'thin', 'longer' 'shorter' and record on the whiteboard/working wall.

6. Introduce the activity to the children by sharing problem prompt poster 14a.

7. Allow time for children to work on the activity together. Ensure the children are encouraged to use the shape properties discussed earlier.

8. During the activity, draw the whole class's attention to any particularly effective description used by the children in the class.

9. At the end of the session, bring the children back together and discuss what strategies they found to be the most effective and name the shapes together. *What shape properties were most useful to use? Which shape was hard and easy to describe?*

Developing reasoning

➤ *Which shape that you have described so far has been **hard/easy** to describe/draw? Why is this?*
➤ ***What do you notice** about this shape/the size of this angle/the length of the sides/these sides?*
➤ ***What's the same? What's different** between [pick two or more shapes that have been drawn, or alternatively pick two or more features of one shape]?*
➤ *Give me a property of this shape you could use to help describe it. **Another, another, another.***

Providing differentiation

Support
Children could focus initially on the regular shapes from the resource sheets. They could also be provided with a copy of the shared definition bank created during the shared learning as well as using cm squared paper to draw the shapes onto.

Extension
Children could be challenged to draw their own shapes for their partner to draw and to consider what would be a hard and easy shape for their partner to draw. More able children could also be introduced to measuring angles using a protractor and then describe the shapes using accurate angle sizes.

 Key strategies

2 Another, another, another
4 Hard and Easy
10 What do you notice?
12 What's the same? What's different?

 Problem-solving approaches

Paired work
Think, pair, share

Taking it further

Further work on properties of shapes could follow this activity, including activity 15 Dotty squares.

15 Dotty squares

Learning objective	Reasoning skills	Curriculum link
• Work systematically to identify shapes of different orientations and sizes.	• Solving problems • Working systematically • Finding all possibilities • Conjecturing and convincing	Geometry: properties of shape

The problem

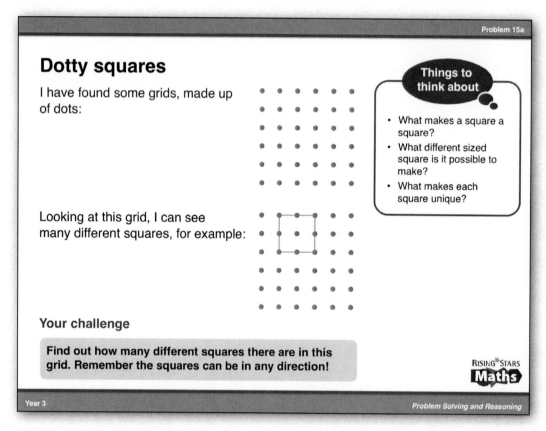

Dotty squares

I have found some grids, made up of dots:

Things to think about

- What makes a square a square?
- What different sized square is it possible to make?
- What makes each square unique?

Looking at this grid, I can see many different squares, for example:

Your challenge

Find out how many different squares there are in this grid. Remember the squares can be in any direction!

RISING STARS
Maths

Year 3

Problem Solving and Reasoning

Problem 15a

Background knowledge

- This problem asks the children to find all the squares which it is possible to make using a 6 × 6 grid of dots. Resource sheet 15.1, Dotty squares (1) provides blank dotty grids for children to use. Using different coloured pencils will help to record children's findings.
- This problem encourages the children to work systematically, as well as to identify shapes in different sizes and orientations.
- Children may choose to start with one size/ orientation square, (e.g. *a 1 × 1 square*) and place this in all possible places on the grid, before moving to the next size square.

- Children should identify squares which are at an angle, as well as of a range of different sizes.

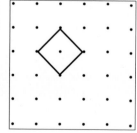

- It is important that children understand what makes a square a square (4 right angles, 4 equal length sides, 2 pairs of parallel sides) and that a square can exist in any orientation.

Launching the activity

1. Display poster prompt 15b, which contains three squares in different orientations. Ask the class: *What's the same? What's different about these different shapes?* Discuss children's responses, ensuring that they understand that all three shapes are squares.

2. Ask the children, *What makes a square, a square?* Identify the different properties of a square, including right angles, equal length sides, parallel and perpendicular sides, etc. Identify that the squares on problem poster 15b are at an angle, still have four right angles, etc.

3. Share the prompt poster 15a with the class and discuss the problem.

4. Ask the children to 'think, pair, share' how they could approach working on the problem, stressing the importance of working systematically and together as a pair/group.

5. Discuss the children's possible strategies with the class.

6. Allow time for the children work on the problem in pairs or small groups.

7. At the end of the activity bring children back together and discuss their findings. Also discuss, what was the largest square that it was possible to make? What was the largest square that was on a diagonal that it possible to make?

Developing reasoning

➤ *Show me a square that is the same dimension of the one you have just found.* **Another, another, another.**

➤ **Convince me** *that you are working in a systematic way/that you have found all possible squares.*

➤ **What do you notice** *about the squares which you have made so far?*

➤ *Give me a* **silly answer** *for a square on this grid? Why is it silly? Can you give me a wrong answer that isn't as silly? Why is this wrong, but not as silly?*

➤ *Give me a* **peculiar and obvious** *square that it is possible to make using this grid.*

Providing differentiation

Support
Children could begin to investigate this problem using a smaller 4 × 4 grid (see Resource sheet 15.2, Dotty squares (2).

Extension
Children should be encouraged to find all squares which are on a diagonal. The children should also be encouraged to complete the activity without recording all possible squares, e.g. visualising the number of 2 × 2 squares that it would be possible to make on the gird. The activity could also be extended to finding different types of shapes, e.g. all rectangles, or all triangles on the grid.

Key strategies

2 Another, another, another
3 Convince me
8 Peculiar, obvious, general,
9 Silly answers
10 What do you notice?

Problem-solving approaches

Paired/small group work
Think, pair, share

Taking it further

The investigation could be followed by further work on properties of shape. Other work on angles could also follow this activity, e.g. problem 14.

16 Cubed aliens

Learning objective	Reasoning skills	Curriculum link
• Work systematically to investigate patterns formed by 3-D shapes.	• Working systematically • Finding all possibilities • Making connections	Geometry: properties of shape

The problem

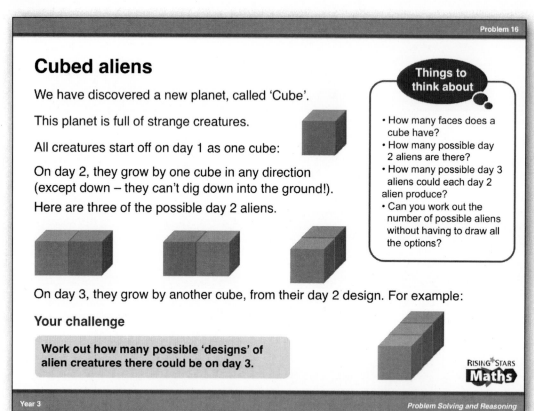

Problem 16

Cubed aliens

We have discovered a new planet, called 'Cube'.

This planet is full of strange creatures.

All creatures start off on day 1 as one cube:

On day 2, they grow by one cube in any direction (except down – they can't dig down into the ground!).

Here are three of the possible day 2 aliens.

On day 3, they grow by another cube, from their day 2 design. For example:

Your challenge

> Work out how many possible 'designs' of alien creatures there could be on day 3.

Things to think about

- How many faces does a cube have?
- How many possible day 2 aliens are there?
- How many possible day 3 aliens could each day 2 alien produce?
- Can you work out the number of possible aliens without having to draw all the options?

RISING STARS
Maths

Year 3   Problem Solving and Reasoning

Background knowledge

- This problem asks the children to work systematically to find all possible designs for a cubed alien.
- The children will need to use their knowledge of the properties of a cube, particularly the number of faces, in order to help them efficiently solve this problem.
- The alien grows by one cube a day, in any direction, except down into the ground, from the last cube that grew.
- This means on day 2, there are five possible 'designs' of alien (see Resource sheet 16.1).
- Children can then use these day 2 designs to work out the number of possible day 3 designs. They can do this by working systematically or by making generalisations.
  - On day 2, there are five possible designs.

- Of these designs, one has five possible faces for a third cube to 'grow' from.
- Of these designs, four have four possible faces for a third cube to 'grow' from (since they can't 'dig' down into the ground).
- There are therefore 21 possible day 3 designs (5 + (4 × 4)).
- If available in your school, the cubed world of Minecraft™ works particularly well to engage children in this activity and as a useful way to record findings. Creations in the game can then be screen shot and printed for evidence. Both the pocket and desktop editions of the game would work for this purpose, and children can join each other's 'world' to work collaboratively on the investigation.
- Some form of construction cubes (interlocking cubes or similar) are essential for children to use during this activity.

Launching the activity

1. Begin by holding up a cube (or giving a cube to each child). Ask the children to work in pairs to describe the cube. Discuss their descriptions together, making sure correct mathematical vocabulary is used.

2. Introduce the problem to the children by sharing the prompt poster.

3. Ask children to 'think, pair, share.' How many possible designs are there for the aliens on day 2?

4. Discuss this together and invite the children to make all possible designs of day 2 aliens using construction cubes/Minecraft™.

5. Once children have made all day 2 'designs', ask them to discuss with a partner possible approaches for working out how many possible day 3 designs there are. Discuss these as a class, drawing attention to the need to work systematically and, if able, make generalisations.

6. Provide time for children to work on this activity, ideally in mixed-ability groups of three or more. Children should either make their designs in Minecraft™ or by using construction cubes.

7. At the end of the session, ask groups to pair up to compare all the designs for day 3 aliens. Can each group convince the other that they have worked systematically and have therefore found all possible designs?

Developing reasoning

➤ **What do you notice** about the number of day 2 designs? **What do you notice** about the number of faces free for a day 3 cube to grow from?

➤ Give me a **peculiar and obvious** day 3 design?

➤ Can you give me a day [2, 3] design? **Another, another, another.**

➤ If we know that there are four possible day 3 designs from this particular day 2 alien, **what else do we know**?

Providing differentiation

Support
Woking in mixed-ability groups, as suggested above, should provide peer support for children who are less confident. Children should also ensure they use construction cubes to represent the problem and may wish to initially focus on day 2 designs, and then systematically work on linked day 3 designs.

Extension
Once children have created a few day 3 designs, they should be encouraged to work out the remainder of possible designs for day 3 by making generalisations, as modelled above in the teacher guidance. They could also extend the problem by looking at day 4 aliens, again making generalisations and predictions.

Key strategies

2 Another, another, another
8 Peculiar and obvious
10 What do you notice?
11 What else do we know?

Problem-solving approaches

Mixed-ability groups

Taking it further

This activity can make an attractive display, if further 'days' of the aliens life are explored. It also provides an opportunity for children to use isometric paper as an alternative recording method.

17 Fastest legs

Learning objective	**Reasoning skills**	**Curriculum link**
• Collect data, including taking accurate measurements, in order to investigate a statement.	• Solving problems • Making comparisons	Measures: statistics

The problem

Problem 17

Fastest legs

Mackenzie and Finlay were watching the races at our last sports day and looked at who won each race.

Finlay said that she thought that the people who won each race were the people with the longest legs.

But Mackenzie thought it depended on more things than this.

I wonder who is right?

Things to think about

- How are you going to carry out this investigation?
- What do you need to measure?
- How many different people do you need to 'investigate' in order to answer the statement?
- How are you going to record and report your results?

Your challenge

Design, carry out and report on an investigation to find out if people with longest legs are always, sometimes or never the fastest runners?

RISING STARS
Maths

Year 3

Problem Solving and Reasoning

Background knowledge

- This problem asks the children to investigate the statement 'Are people with the longest legs, always, sometimes or never the fastest runners?'
- The children will need to decide how to carry out this investigation. They should ideally measure the leg length of a range of different people in the class, then time them running over a set distance and then compare the results.

- The results of this investigation are best presented in a table, comparing leg length to time over the set distance. You may also wish to take the data and, using ICT, present on a scatter graph to illustrate how the data could also be presented.
- The investigation could also be carried out as a whole class, with the children working in pairs to measure leg length and running time, before collating the results together.
- Through the investigation, children should focus on choosing appropriate units of measure and taking accurate measurements.

Launching the activity

1. Share the problem prompt poster with the class. Ask children to discuss with their partner if they thought the statement was always, sometimes or never true. Discuss this and the children's initial conjectures as a class.

2. Ask the children to 'think, pair, share.' How could we design an investigation in order to investigate this problem?

3. Discuss the children's initial ideas as a class, drawing attention to the need for accurate measurements. Establish that they will need to measure leg length, a length of a course to run and the time taken to run the course.

4. Ask the children what units would be most appropriate to record:
   - leg length
   - length of the course
   - time take to run the course.

5. Discuss the choice of units with the children, asking why it would not be more appropriate to use other units.

6. Allow children plenty of time to carry out the investigation, working in mixed-ability groups of at least four.

7. Support groups as necessary, ensuring that each group considers the units, taking accurate measurements, and how they are going to record and present their data.

8. At the end of the activity, bring children back together and discuss each group's findings. *Is the statement always, sometimes or never true?*

9. You may also wish to collate the different findings from each group and analyse these as a class.

Developing reasoning

➤ *Is the statement always, sometimes or never true? Can we say it is always true?*
➤ *Convince me that this is the most appropriate way to measure/is the most appropriate unit to choose/you are measuring accurately.*
➤ *What do you notice about the relationship between leg length and running speed?*
➤ *What else do we know by looking at the data you have collected?*

Providing differentiation

Support
The mixed-ability grouping in this activity should provide peer scaffolding for children. Panic envelopes could also be used, providing different hints/tips for carrying out the investigation.

Extension
The children could extend this investigation to investigate the effects of other factors, e.g. age, overall height, on running speed.

Key strategies

1 Always, sometimes, never
3 Convince me
10 What do you notice?
11 What else do we know?

Problem-solving approaches

Mixed-ability grouping
Think, pair, share
Panic envelopes

Taking it further

This investigation could be used as the springboard into further sports related investigations. NRICH provide a selection of sports related activities here: http://nrich.maths.org/thismonth/all/2012/01

18 Chocolate swap!

Learning objective	Reasoning skills	Curriculum link
• Collect and present statistics and consider what information can be gained from the statistics collected.	• Solving problems • Making comparisons • Conjecturing and convincing	**x=** Statistics: interpreting data

The problem

Chocolate swap!

I LOVE chocolate. In fact, I spent so much time eating chocolate (and watching films!) this weekend, that I forgot to write some questions for today's statistics lesson. I'd normally give you some data and some questions to answer based on it.

But, I was wondering if we could switch roles? Could you give me some data about chocolate and then some questions that I could answer based on it?

Things to think about

- What are you going to investigate?
- How are you going to present your data?
- What can you tell from the data you have presented?

Your challenge

Collect some data based on chocolate, present it in some way, and write some questions which could be answered based on the data you have presented.

Year 3   Problem Solving and Reasoning

Background knowledge

- This problem asks children to collect some data, based around the theme of chocolate, present it and create some questions which can be answered based on the data they have presented.
- Ideally this activity would extend over more than one lesson.
- The children should have some experience of answering questions based on data before carrying out this activity.
- Example questions which the children could investigate include '*What is the favourite chocolate bar in our class?*', '*Do people prefer milk, dark or white chocolate?*', or '*How much chocolate do people eat each week?*'

- The children will probably choose to present the data as a bar graph or pictogram, which meets the requirements of the program of study. ICT could be used to help children present their data.
- When asking questions, the children should be encouraged to write a range of questions, including single step questions (e.g. *How many people like x? What is the most popular?*) and multi-step questions (e.g. *How many more people like x than y? How many people did we ask in total?*).

Launching the activity

1. Share the problem prompt poster with the class adding extra drama if possible!

2. Ask children to 'think, pair, share' the different steps they will need to go through in order to investigate this problem. Discuss this as a class.

3. Ask children to discuss with a partner some ideas of statements which they could investigate. Discuss the children's ideas as a class, making notes of suggestions for questions to investigate on the whiteboard and/or working wall.

4. Ask the children how they could present their data. Ask them **what's the same? What's different** between the different methods they suggest?

5. Allow time for children to work in mixed-ability groups to plan, carry out and present their data, supporting each group as needed and developing reasoning.

6. Once children have collected and presented data, bring them back together. If possible, share one group's data and graphs/tables/pictograms. Ask children: What do you notice by looking at the data? Model how statements given by children could be turned into questions which could be answered from data collected, including how multi-step and more advanced questions could be created.

7. Provide time for each group to work on creating questions based on the data which they collected earlier.

8. At the end of the activity ask children to swap data and questions, and to attempt to answer each other's questions.

9. Ask each group to share the 'best' question from the data and question set which they now have in front of them and to justify why they think this is the 'best' question.

Developing reasoning

➤ *Give me something you can tell from this data.* **Another, another, another.**

➤ *Is it* **always, sometimes** *or* **never** *true that ... [pick statement from the data]?*

➤ **What do you notice** *about [pick element of data that has been collected]?*

➤ **What else do we know** *by looking at the data you have collected?*

➤ *Give me a* **silly questions** *that you couldn't answer based on the data you have collected. Why is this a silly question?*

➤ *Give me a* **peculiar and obvious** *question which you could ask based on the data you have collected. What makes them peculiar/obvious?*

Providing differentiation

Support

The mixed-ability grouping in this activity should provide peer scaffolding for children. Panic envelopes could also be used, providing different questions to investigate and hints/tips of how to carry out investigations and present data. For the creating questions element, children may need closer questioning and guidance.

Extension

Children should be encouraged to create multi-step questions based on the data, as well as linking other areas of learning, e.g. proportionality, into the questions they are asking.

 Key strategies

1 Always, sometimes, never
2 Another, another, another
8 Peculiar, obvious, general
9 Silly answers
10 What do you notice?
11 What else do we know?

 Problem-solving approaches

Mixed-ability grouping
Think, pair, share
Panic envelopes

Taking it further

The investigation could also be followed by further work on statistics, e.g. problem 17.

Glossary

Commutative An operation which can be carried out in any order without affecting the result. Addition and multiplication are commutative, e.g.
4 x 3 = 3 x 4 and 8 + 7 = 7 + 8.

Conjecture A thought or idea about a pattern, solution or relationship. Children should be encouraged to form conjectures about maths, e.g. 'My conjecture is that the answer will always be a product of the other numbers' and then to convince themselves and their peers that their conjecture is true.

Denominator The bottom number in a fraction. This shows how many equal parts the whole is split into.

Digit Digits are 0, 1, 2, 3, 4, 5, 6, 7, 8, 9. Their position within a number determines their value.

Digit root The number formed when continuously finding the digit sum until a single digit number is formed, e.g. the digit root of 789 is 6 (7 + 8 + 9 = 24, 2 + 4 = 6).

Digit sum The number formed when all the digits in a number are added (as if each digit were in the ones place), e.g. the digit sum of 789 is 24 (7 + 8 + 9).

Factor Factors of a number are numbers which multiply together to give that number and usually come in pairs, e.g. the factors of 24 are 1 and 24, 2 and 12, 3 and 8, 4 and 6.

Fraction A way of showing a proportion of a whole. Fractions take the form ½ and are made up of a numerator and denominator. A fraction splits the whole into equal parts.

Multiple A number which can be divided by another number without leaving a remainder, e.g. 6 is a multiple of 360 as 360 ÷ 6 = 60.

Number Numbers are digits which have been assigned a place value, e.g. the digits 3, 5 and 6 can be arranged to make the number 563 with the digit 5 having a value of 500 or 5 hundreds, the digit 6 having the value of 60 or 6 tens and the digit 3 having the value of 3 or 3 ones.

Numerator The top number in a fraction. This shows how many of the equal parts you 'have'.

Partitioning Breaking up a number into smaller numbers. Partitioning can be canonical, which means breaking multiples of 10, 100, 1000, etc (e.g. 878 partitioned canonically would be 800 + 70 + 8, or 400 + 400 + 70 + 8) or non-canonically which means partitioning into numbers which are not all multiples of 10, 100, 1000, etc (e.g. 878 = 450 + 350 + 35 + 35 + 6 + 2).

Polygon An enclosed shape with 3 or more straight sides. Regular polygons have equal sides and angles. Irregular polygons are those where the sides and angles differ in size.

Prime Prime numbers have only two factors: 1 and the number itself.

Product The result when multiplying two or more numbers together, e.g. the product of 3, 4 and 2 is 24.

Quadrilateral A 4-sided polygon.

Rectangle A quadrilateral with 4 right angles and 2 pairs of equal and parallel sides. A square is a special type of rectangle with 4 equal sides.

Square numbers Square numbers have an odd number of factors, as they can be formed by multiplying a number by itself, e.g. 16 is a square number, as it is the product of 4 x 4.

Sum The total when adding two or more numbers together, e.g. the sum of 5 + 6 is 11. 'Sums' do not refer to any type of calculation other than addition.

Systematically The act of working in an ordered and considered way, especially when tackling a problem or investigation, e.g. when exploring numbers which sum to 100, a systematic way of working would be to start with 100 + 0, then 99 + 1, 98 + 2, 97 + 3, etc.